C000200582

Also by Judith Schalansky in English translation

Atlas of Remote Islands
The Giraffe's Neck

Judith Schalansky

AN INVENTORY
OF LOSSES

Translated from the German by
Jackie Smith

MACLEHOSE PRESS
A Bill Swainson Book
QUERCUS · LONDON

First published in the German language as
Verzeichnis einiger Verluste by
Suhrkamp Verlag, Berlin, in 2018

First published in Great Britain in 2020 as

A Bill Swainson Book
by
MacLehose Press
An imprint of Quercus Publishing Ltd
Carmelite House
50 Victoria Embankment
London EC4Y 0DZ

An Hachette UK company

The translation of this work was supported by a grant from the Goethe-Institut

GOETHE
INSTITUT

ISBN (HB) 978 1 52940 079 3
ISBN (Ebook) 978 1 52940 077 9

10 9 8 7 6 5 4 3 2 1

Designed and typeset in Fabiol Pro and Weissenhof Grotesk bold
by Libanus Press, Marlborough
Printed and bound in Italy by L.E.G.O. S.p.A.

CONTENTS

Preamble   7

Preface   11

Tuanaki   29

Caspian Tiger   47

Guericke's Unicorn   65

Villa Sacchetti   83

The Boy in Blue   101

The Love Songs of Sappho   119

The Von Behr Palace   137

The Seven Books of Mani   155

Greifswald Harbour   173

Encyclopaedia in the Wood   191

Palace of the Republic   209

Kinau's Selenographs   227

Index of Persons   245

Index of Images and Sources   252

PREAMBLE

While I was working on this book, the Cassini spacecraft burned up in Saturn's atmosphere; the Schiaparelli Mars lander crashed in the rust-coloured rocky landscape of the planet it was supposed to be exploring; a Boeing 777 disappeared without trace en route from Kuala Lumpur to Beijing; in Palmyra, the 2,000-year-old Temples of Baal and Baalshamin, the façade of the Roman theatre, the Monumental Arch, the tetrapylon and parts of the Great Colonnade were blown up; in Mosul, Iraq, the Great Mosque of al-Nuri and the Mosque of the Prophet Jonah were destroyed and in Syria the Early Christian Monastery of St Elian was reduced to rubble; in Kathmandu an earthquake caused the Dharahara Tower to collapse for the second time; a third of the Great Wall of China fell victim to vandalism and erosion; unknown perpetrators stole the head from the corpse of Friedrich Wilhelm Murnau; Guatemala's Lake Atescatempa, once renowned for its blue-green waters, dried up; the arch-like rock formation on the coast of Malta known as the Azure Window collapsed into the Mediterranean; the Bramble Cay mosaic-tailed rat, native to the Great Barrier Reef, became extinct; the last-known male northern white rhinoceros had to be put to sleep at the age of forty-five, survived by only two specimens of this subspecies: his daughter and his granddaughter; the only existing sample of metallic hydrogen, obtained after eighty years of fruitless efforts, disappeared from a laboratory at Harvard University, and no-one knows whether the microscopically small particle was stolen or destroyed or simply reverted to a gaseous state.

While I was working on this book, an archivist at New York's
Schaffer Library found in an almanac dating from 1793 an enve-
lope containing several strands of grey hair belonging to George
Washington; a hitherto unknown Walt Whitman novel and the lost
album *Both Directions at Once* by jazz saxophonist John Coltrane
came to light; a nineteen-year-old intern discovered hundreds
of Piranesi drawings in Karlsruhe State Museum's collection of
works on paper; a double page of Anne Frank's Diary which had
brown paper pasted over it was successfully deciphered; the
world's oldest alphabet, carved on stone tablets 3,800 years ago,
was identified; image data were successfully reconstructed from
the photographs taken in 1966–7 by the Lunar Orbiters; fragments
were discovered of two hitherto unknown poems by Sappho;
ornithologists recorded several sightings, in a Brazilian tree
savanna, of blue-eyed ground doves which had been presumed
extinct since 1941; biologists discovered the wasp species *Deuter-
agenia ossarium*, which builds multichamber nests in hollow tree
trunks for its young, placing a dead spider ready in each chamber
as a source of nutrition; in the Arctic the wrecks of H.M.S. *Erebus*
and *Terror* from the ill-fated 1848 Franklin Expedition were located; archaeologists in northern Greece unearthed an enormous
burial mound, the final resting place probably not of Alexander
the Great but possibly of his companion Hephaestion; Mahen-
draparvata, the first Khmer capital, thought to have been the
largest settlement of the Middle Ages, was discovered close to
the Angkor Wat temple complex in Cambodia; archaeologists
working in the necropolis of Saqqara happened upon a mummifi-
cation workshop; in the Cygnus constellation, 1,400 light years
from our sun, a celestial body was found, in a so-called habitable
zone, on which the average temperature is similar to that of Earth,
meaning there may be or may once have been water there, and
hence also life, such as we imagine life to be.

PREFACE

On an August day a few years ago I visited a town in the north. It lies on one of the innermost bays of a marine inlet that has extended far into the interior of the land since a prehistoric ice age, and whose brackish water is home in spring to herring, in summer to eels, in autumn to cod and in winter to carp, pike and bream, hence fishermen ply their trade there to this day. For centuries these men and their families have lived in a neighbourhood that can only be described as quaint, consisting of little more than two cobbled streets, a drying place for the nets and a monastery now occupied only by two aristocratic old ladies. In short, it is one of those seemingly timeless places that might very well tempt one to believe that some bygone age as vague as it is appealing is still alive today. Yet it was not the flowering rose-bushes and leggy hollyhocks in front of the squat, whitewashed houses, nor their brightly painted wooden doors or the narrow alleys between the buildings, most of them leading straight down to the stony shore, that particularly lodged in my memory, but rather the peculiar fact that, in the village centre, instead of a market square, I found a graveyard, shaded by the green foliage of young lime trees and enclosed by cast-iron railings, in other words the fact that, in the place where normally goods would be exchanged for money, instead the dead and buried were doing what, out of entrenched wishful thinking, is generally termed "resting in peace". My astonishment, which I initially took for unease, was considerable and was further compounded when someone pointed out to me the house of a woman who, while she cooked, was able to look out from her kitchen upon the grave of her prematurely deceased son, and it became clear to me that the centuries-old tradition of the guild that takes care of the funeral rites here had resulted in the dead and the living of the same family ending up in the kind of close proximity I had previously only heard of in the case of the inhabitants of certain Pacific islands. Of course I had visited other notable burial sites before: the cemetery island of San Michele, for instance, which, with its high red-brick walls, looms up out of the turquoise water of the lagoon of Venice like an impenetrable fortress, or the garish stalls in the Hollywood Forever Cemetery to mark the *Día de los Muertos* celebrated annually by the Mexican people, with graves decked out in orange and yellow, and skulls made from brightly coloured sugar and papier mâché, doomed by their advanced state of decay to grin in perpetuity. Yet none touched me as deeply as the fishing community's cemetery, whose peculiar shape — a kind of compromise between a circle and a square — struck me as the very emblem of the remarkable utopia I saw embodied there: a life where death was always in view. For a long time I was convinced that in this place, whose Danish name means "small island" or "surrounded by water", one is closer to life, precisely because its inhabitants had literally brought the dead into their midst instead of — as is otherwise the norm in our latitudes — banishing them from the heart of the community to beyond the city gates, although these burial sites often became reintegrated into the urban environment only a short time later, the result of unchecked urban sprawl.

Only now, having almost finished work on this book in which the diverse phenomena of decomposition and destruction play a central role, have I realised that this is just one of myriad ways of dealing with death, one that is fundamentally no more crude or caring than that of the Callatiae tribe whose custom, as Herodotus attests, was to eat their deceased parents, and who were horrified when they learned of the Greeks' tradition of cremating theirs. Indeed opinions differ as to who is closer to life: someone constantly reminded of his own mortality or someone who manages to suppress all thought of it, and likewise on the question of which is more terrifying: the notion that everything comes to an end, or the thought that it may not.

There is no disputing, though, that death and the associated problem of how to deal with the sudden absence of a person at the same time as the presence of their legacy, from the corpse to the abandoned belongings, have, over time, demanded answers and prompted actions which have had a significance beyond their strict purpose, and which mark the elevation of our early ancestors from the animal to the human sphere. Not simply giving over the mortal remains of the fellow members of our species to the natural processes of decomposition is generally regarded as something peculiar to humans, although similar behaviour can also be observed in other higher animals: elephants, for instance, gather around a dying member of their herd, touch it with their trunks for hours on end, trumpeting in distress as they do so, and often try to push the lifeless body back upright before eventually covering the corpse with earth and twigs. What's more, they return to the place of death regularly, even years later, something that undoubtedly requires a good memory, and possibly even a certain conception of the afterlife which, it is fair to imagine, is no less fanciful than our own and just as unverifiable.

The caesura of death is the point where legacy and memory begin, and the lament the source of every culture by which we seek to fill the now gaping void, the sudden silence with chants, prayers and stories in which the absent one is brought back to life. Like a hollow mould, the experience of loss renders visible the contours of the thing mourned, and it is not uncommon for it to be transformed by the transfigurative light of sorrow into an object of desire or, as the Heidelberg professor of zoology put it in the foreword to a slim volume published by Neue Brehm-Bücherei: "It seems to be one of the characteristics of western man that defies rational understanding that he prizes the lost more highly than the existing. There is no other explanation for his curious enduring fascination with the Tasmanian tiger."

All manner of strategies are used to keep hold of the past and ward off oblivion. If tradition is to be believed, our historiography begins with a series of devastating wars between the Persians and the Greeks, while the now almost forgotten art of memory starts with an accident in which many perished: it was in Thessaly, where in the early fifth century B.C. a collapsing house buried an entire party of festive revellers and the only survivor, the poet Simonides of Ceos, succeeded, with the aid of his trained memory, in re-entering the destroyed building in his mind's eye and recalling the seating arrangement of the guests, thus enabling the bodies crushed beyond recognition by the falling rubble to be identified. It is one of the numerous paradoxes inherent in the either-or of life and death that, by labelling the deceased as something irretrievably lost, the sorrow at this loss is at once doubled and halved, whereas the indeterminate fate of a person missing or presumed dead keeps the relatives trapped in a confused nightmare of anxious hope and denied sorrow that makes it impossible either to come to terms with it or to get on with one's life.

Being alive means experiencing loss. The question of what the future holds is presumably nearly as old as the human race itself, given that one feature of the future, as inevitable as it is disquieting, is that it defies prediction and hence gives no clue as to the timing and circumstances of death. Who can deny the protective magic of bittersweet anticipation, the fatal urge to forestall the

feared event by mentally pre-empting it? We picture the cataclysm ahead of time, imagine possible disasters and believe this
renders us immune to nasty surprises. In ancient times, dreams
promised consolation: the Greeks said of them that, like oracles,
they prefigured what was to come and thereby rid the future not
of its immutability, but at least of the terror of the unexpected.
Quite a few people take their own life out of fear of death.
Suicide seems perhaps the most radical means of conquering the
uncertainty of the future, albeit at the cost of a curtailed existence.
It is reported that the gifts presented by the Indian delegation
that Augustus once received on the island of Samos included not
only a tiger and an armless youth who was able to use his feet as
hands, but also a man named Zarmarus from the Brahmin caste
who was intending to end his own life for the very reason that it
had turned out the way he wanted. To make quite sure that no
calamity could ever befall him, he leaped onto the pyre in Athens,
naked, anointed, and with a smile, was burned alive, undoubtedly
in excruciating pain, and in staging his self-determined death,
went down in history, if only as a curious anecdote in one book of
Cassius Dio's once eighty-volume *Roman History*, the content
of which happened to be passed down to us. In the end, all that
remains is simply whatever is left.

A memory that retained everything would essentially retain nothing. The Californian woman who, without the aid of mnemonics,
can recall every single day since February 5, 1980 is trapped in the
echo chamber of the memories that constantly overwhelm her –
a modern embodiment of that Athenian general Themistocles,
who knew the names of every single citizen of his native city and
who told Simonides, the father of mnemonics, that he would
rather learn the art of forgetting than that of remembering: "I
remember even what I do not want to remember, but am unable

to forget what I want to forget." However, the art of forgetting is an impossibility because any allusion represents a presence, even when it refers to an absence. Encyclopaedias claim to know the names of almost every person condemned to *damnatio memoriae* under the Roman Empire.

To forget everything is bad, certainly. Worse still is to forget nothing. After all, knowledge can only be gained by forgetting. If everything is stored indiscriminately, as it is in electronic data memories, it loses its meaning and becomes a disorderly mass of useless information.

The organisation of every archive may, like its prototype, the ark, be guided by the desire to preserve everything, but the undeniably tempting idea of transforming, say, a continent like the Antarctic or even the moon into a central, democratic museum of the Earth in which all cultural products are accorded equal status is just as totalitarian and doomed to failure as the re-creation of paradise, a tantalising primal object of longing kept alive in the beliefs of all human cultures.

Fundamentally, every item is already waste, every building already a ruin, and all creation nothing but destruction, and the same is true of the work of all those disciplines and institutions that claim to be preserving the legacy of humanity. Even archaeology, however cautiously and soberly it may profess to probe the debris of past ages, is a form of devastation – and the archives, museums and libraries, the zoological gardens and nature reserves are nothing more than managed cemeteries whose stored specimens, as often as not, have been plucked from the lifecycle of the present to be filed away, allowed to be forgotten even, like those heroic events and figures whose monuments populate urban landscapes.

It should probably count as a good thing that the human race is not aware of all the great ideas, the poignant works of art and revolutionary feats that have already been lost to it – wilfully destroyed or simply vanished over time. What we do not know cannot weigh us down, we might think. It does seem surprising, though, that quite a few European thinkers of the modern age saw the periodic demise of a culture as a reasonable or even beneficial occurrence. As if cultural memory were a global organism whose vital functions could only be maintained by a brisk metabolism in which each intake of food was preceded by digestion and elimination.

It was this world view, one both limited and autocratic, that enabled the uncontrolled occupation and exploitation of foreign territories, the subjugation, enslavement and murder of non-European peoples and the obliteration of their scorned cultures to be regarded as part of a natural process, and the evolutionary principle misunderstood as meaning the survival of the strongest to be used as justification for crimes committed.

Naturally we can only mourn what is absent or missing if some vestige of it, some whisper, perhaps little more than a rumour, a semi-obliterated trace, an echo of an echo has found its way to us. How I would love to know what the Nazca lines in the Peruvian desert mean, how Sappho's Fragment 31 ends, and why Hypatia was considered such a threat that not only her complete works but even she herself was hacked to pieces.

Sometimes certain remnants seem to be commenting on their own fate. For instance, all that remains of Monteverdi's opera "L'Arianna" is, of all things, the *lamento*, in which the eponymous heroine sings in despair: "Let me die! What do you think can comfort me in such harsh fate, in such great suffering? Let me die!" The picture by Lucian Freud that now survives only as a reproduction since it was stolen from a Rotterdam museum and incinerated in a Romanian stove by the mother of one of the thieves, shows a woman with her eyes closed, and one cannot tell for sure whether she is just sleeping or is actually dead. And of the work of the tragic poet Agathon only two aphorisms have found their way to us, because they are quoted by Aristotle: "Art loves chance and chance loves art" and "Not even the gods can change the past".

That which is denied the gods is something that despots through the ages all seem to aspire to anew: the destructive drive to make their mark is not satisfied by inscribing themselves in the present. Anyone who wants to control the future must obliterate the past. And anyone who appoints himself the founding father of a new dynasty, the source of all truth, must eradicate the memory of his predecessors and forbid all critical thinking, as Qin Shi Huang, the self-appointed "First Sovereign Emperor", did when in 213 B.C. he ordered one of the first recorded book burnings and had anyone who opposed the measure executed or sentenced to forced labour, working on the expansion of the imperial road network and the Great Wall of China – or other-wise on the construction of that colossal mausoleum whose meg-alomaniac funerary art includes the Terracotta Army of life-size soldiers along with their chariots, horses and weaponry, copies of which now tour the world, thereby both fulfilling and under-mining the purpose of the memorial its patron had so craved by untold profanation.

The dubious plan to make a *tabula rasa* of the past often springs from the understandable desire to start afresh. Apparently, in the mid-seventeenth century, the British parliament seriously discussed burning the Tower of London archives to extinguish all memory of the past and start life over again, at least according to Jorge Luis Borges in a passage I have been unable to locate.

The Earth itself is, as we know, a heap of rubble from a past future, and humanity the thrown-together, bickering community of heirs to a numinous yesteryear that needs to be constantly appropriated and recast, rejected and destroyed, ignored and suppressed so that, contrary to popular belief, it is not the future but the past that represents the true field of opportunity. That is precisely why its reinterpretation is one of the first official acts of new governing regimes. Anyone who, like me, has experienced a historical upheaval, the iconoclasm of the victors, the dismantling of monuments, will readily recognise every vision of the future as effectively representing a future past in which, say, the ruins of the rebuilt Berlin City Palace will have to make way for a replica of the demolished Palace of the Republic.

At the Paris Salon of 1796, in the fifth year of the Republic, the architecture painter Hubert Robert, who had captured the storming of the Bastille as well as the demolition of the Château de Meudon and the desecration of the royal tombs in Saint-Denis, exhibited two paintings in the Palais du Louvre. One depicted his proposed design for the transformation of the royal palace to create the *Grande Galerie* – a room packed with paintings and sculptures, teeming with visitors and flooded with light thanks to its glass roof – while the other painting showed the same room in ruins. The skylights visible in the first vision of the future are replaced in the second by an uninterrupted view of a cloudy sky: the arched roof has caved in, the walls are bare and unadorned, broken sculptures lie on the floor. Only the Apollo Belvedere, a trophy from Napoleon's Italian foray, is left standing among the rubble, sooty but unscathed. Disaster tourists wander among the ruins, salvage toppled torsos, warm themselves by a fire. Weeds sprout from the cracks in the vault. The ruins are a utopian place in which past and future become one.

The architect Albert Speer went even further with his speculative theory of a "ruin value": decades after the end of National Socialism, he claimed that its plans for, literally, a thousand-year Reich would not only have made use of exceptionally durable materials, but would even have taken into account the future appearance of each building once it fell to ruin, so that, even in a dilapidated state, it could still compete with the grandeur of the Roman ruins. Auschwitz, on the other hand, was referred to, for good reason, as a case of destruction without ruins. It was the utterly dehumanised architecture of a minutely organised industrial annihilation machine whose workings left no trace which, by exterminating millions of people, left behind the biggest void in Europe in the twentieth century, a trauma still not fully processed in the memory of the survivors and their descendants on either the victims' or the perpetrators' side, one which forms a dissociated foreign body that resists integration. The genocides committed have lent added urgency to the question of the extent to which loss can ever be made tangible and have led many from later generations to the frustrating yet understandable conclusion that what happened eludes all representation.

"What do historical sources preserve? Not the fates of the violets trodden underfoot in the Battle of Liège, nor the sufferings of the cows as Leuven burned, nor the cloud formations on the approach to Belgrade," writes Theodor Lessing in his book *History: Making Sense of the Senseless*, published during the First World War, in which he exposes the chapters in any history that advances in a reasonable way as retrospectively giving form to the formless – stories of beginnings and endings, of ascendancy and downfall, of blossoming and decay which tend to follow narrative rules.

The fact that faith in progress, the legacy of the Enlightenment, persists virtually intact, even though the principles of evolution have shown that what survives for a certain time is determined, rather, by a disturbingly complex interplay of chance and adaptation, is perhaps due to the simple appeal of the nerdy historical timeline and its equivalents in the linear scripts of western cultures – which make it all too easy to fall prey to the naturalistic fallacy, despite the loss of significance of the divine entities, of perceiving everything that exists as intended and meaningful. In the simple-minded yet compelling script of ceaseless advancement, the only use for the past consists in it being inferior to the present, whereby history – the history of one's own life or of a nation or of the human race – is imagined as representing necessary, or at least not random, progress. It has been proved however that, as every archivist knows, chronology – the allocation of sequential numbers for each new addition – is in its banal logic the most unoriginal of all organisational principles, being only a simulation of order.

In a sense, the world is a sprawling archive of itself – and all animate and inanimate matter serves as documentary evidence forming part of a monstrous, highly tedious inscription system that attempts to draw lessons and conclusions from past experience, while taxonomy is merely the retrospective attempt to index the muddled archive of biological diversity by keyword and impose an apparently objective structure on the sheer inexhaustible chaos of evolutionary legacy. Fundamentally, nothing can be lost in this archive, because its overall energy level is constant and everything seems to leave a trace somewhere. If there is truth in Sigmund Freud's perplexing dictum – reminiscent of the law of energy conservation – that no dream and no thought is ever really forgotten, then not only could past experience – an inherited trauma, two random lines from a poem, a hazy nightmare from a stormy night in early childhood, a pornographic horror scenario – be exhumed from the soil of human memory by an effort akin to an archaeological dig in the same way as bones, fossils or fragments of pottery. It might also be possible to wrest from the underworld the actions of countless lost races, if only one started to look for traces of them, in which case the truth, even that which has been suppressed or obliterated, recast as a mistake or consigned to oblivion, could not be denied and would remain ever-present.

Yet the laws of physics offer only limited consolation. For the principle of energy conservation with its triumph of transformation over the finite fails to mention that most conversion processes are irreversible. What use is the heat of a burning artwork? Its ashes will retain nothing worthy of admiration. Those billiard balls fashioned from the recycled, desilverised material used to record early silent movies roll over the green felt-covered table with indifference. The meat of the last Steller's sea cow did not take long to digest.

True, the demise of all life and endeavour is a condition of its existence. It is naturally only a matter of time before everything has disappeared, disintegrated and decayed, before everything is annihilated and destroyed, even those peculiar products of the past whose existence we owe entirely to disasters: the only documents written in the long unfathomable, pictogram-style ancient Greek syllabic script, Linear B, which have been preserved only because the major fire that destroyed the Palace of Knossos in around 1380 B.C. at the same time caused thousands of clay tablets on which the palace's income and expenditure were recorded to harden, thereby preserving them for future generations; the plaster casts of people and animals buried alive in Pompeii when Vesuvius erupted whose corpses, having decomposed, left fillable cavities in the set stone; or the silhouettes left like ghostly photographs on walls and road surfaces in Hiroshima by people vaporised when the atomic bomb went off.

To acknowledge one's own mortality is painful, and the vain urge to defy the transience of life and leave traces for unknown future generations, to remain in memory, "unforgotten", according to the valiant declaration of intent chiselled into the granite of gravestones, is understandable.

The poignant desire to draw attention to the existence of an intelligent species is also manifest in the messages carried by the two time capsules on board the *Voyager I* and *Voyager II* space probes as they drift further and further into interstellar space. The two identical gold-plated copper discs contain images and diagrams, pieces of music and sounds, as well as spoken greetings in fifty-five different languages, the intrepid awkwardness of which – "Hello from the children of the planet Earth" – reveals much about humanity. There is a certain appeal in imagining that all that will one day remain of humanity is Mozart's "Queen of the Night" aria, Louis Armstrong's "Melancholy Blues" and the blare of Azerbaijani bagpipes, assuming the extraterrestrial finders succeed in both deciphering and following the instructions for playing the analogue-encoded record, which are engraved on the disc in diagrammatic form. The likelihood of this, as the authors of this space-age message in a bottle themselves conceded, is so slim that this undertaking can be viewed as the product of a kind of magical thinking that lives on in the scientific community which, in this project, has staged a ritual that serves first and foremost as a means of self-reassurance for a species unwilling to accept its own utter meaninglessness. But what use is an archive without a reader, a time capsule without a finder, an inheritance without inheritors? Experience shows that it is the discarded rubbish of past ages that proves most enlightening to archaeologists. Forming a geological layer of technological junk, plastic and nuclear waste, it will stand the test of time without our assistance, provide genuine information about our habits, and burden the planet for generations to come.

It may be that, by then, our descendants will have long since relocated to that second Earth we have yearned for since time immemorial, which would enable us to turn back time, put right past mistakes and if need be painstakingly recreate all that was thoughtlessly destroyed. And perhaps by then the cultural legacy of the human race will actually be stored as artificial D.N.A. in the genetic material of a particularly resistant strain of bacteria.

There exists a papyrus roll dating from the middle years of the first Egyptian dynasty in around 2900 B.C. that, owing to its precarious state of preservation, has not been opened to this day, so we cannot know what message it contains. Sometimes I imagine the future thus: generations to come standing baffled in front of today's data storage media, strange aluminium boxes whose contents, owing to rapid advances in platforms and programming languages, file formats and playback devices, have become nothing but meaningless codes, and moreover ones which, as an object in themselves, exude less of an aura than the knots of an Inca quipu string, as eloquent as they are mute, or those mystifying ancient Egyptian obelisks that may commemorate triumph or tragedy, no-one knows.

Although nothing lasts for ever, some things do endure longer than others: churches and temples survive longer than palaces, and written cultures outlive those that got by without complex semiotic systems. Writing, which the Khwarezmian scholar Al-Biruni once described as a being propagating itself in time and space, was from the outset a system for passing on information in parallel with inheritance and irrespective of kinship.

By writing, as by reading, one can pick one's own ancestors and establish a second, intellectual hereditary line to rival conventional biological heritage.

If you want to regard the human race itself, as is sometimes suggested, as the world-archiving faculty of a deity, one that preserves awareness of the universe, then the myriad written and printed books – with the exception, of course, of those written by

God himself or his numerous emanations – appear as attempts to discharge this futile duty and capture the infinite nature of all things within their finite bodies.

It may be due merely to my inadequate powers of imagination that the book still appears to me as the most complete of all media, even though paper, in use for several centuries now, is not as durable as papyrus, parchment, stone, ceramic or quartz, and not even the Bible – the most commonly printed, most widely translated collection of writings there is – has been handed down to us in its entirety, though its multiplicity of versions increases the chances of its being passed down for the duration of a few human generations, an open time capsule in which the traces of the time that has passed since it was written and printed are recorded as well, and in which every edition of a text proves to be a utopian space not unlike a ruin in which the dead communicate, the past is alive, the written word is true and time is suspended. The book may be inferior in many ways to the new, seemingly incorporeal media that lay claim to its legacy and overwhelm us with information, and may be a conservative medium in the original sense of the word, but it is the only one which, by the very self-sufficiency of its body, in which text, image and design dovetail perfectly with one another, promises to lend order to the world or sometimes even to take its place. The theological division of being into a mortal and immortal part – the body and soul – may be one of the most consoling strategies for overcoming loss. However, for me, the inseparability of form and content is the reason why I like not only to write but also to design books.

This book, like all others, springs from the desire to have something survive, to bring the past into the present, to call to mind the forgotten, to give voice to the silenced and to mourn the lost. Writing cannot bring anything back, but it can enable everything to be experienced. Hence this volume is as much about seeking as finding, as much about losing as gaining, and gives a sense that the difference between presence and absence is perhaps marginal, as long as there is memory.

For a few precious moments during the long years of working on this book, the notion that all things must pass struck me as just as consoling as the image of all the copies of it gathering dust on the shelves.

Insel ?

Tutuaoa

Union I.

10

Pukapuka (Danger I.)

*Tema Riff

Nassau I.?

Swarrow I. I.

Olosenga

Manua *Rose
(s. Carton westl. Hll.)

Samoa

Schiffer I.

Drei Inseln ?

*Iuul (Savage) I.

Beveridge Rf.
(Nicholson)

20

Hervey (Cook) I.

Haran Riff ?

Thomson ?

Hamond ?

30

40

*Tongarewa (Penrhy

Manihiki Inse

*Rakaanga

Manihiki (Humphrey)

Insel ?

Bellingshausen (Ururutu) Ges
Scilly I. (Fenuaura) s. C
Mopelia

Palmerston

Aitutaki
*383 Anuta
Hervey I. ? Yenua
Reirea ? Azil *Mitero
*Mauki

*Rarotonga
2900
*Mangea

San
60

*Insel

Tuanaka

*New I. ?

Favorite I. ?

Haymet Felsen.

Maria Theresa Ra

Southern Cook Islands
TUANAKI
also known as *Tuanahe*

** The atoll was situated around two hundred nautical miles south of the
island of Rarotonga and around one hundred nautical miles south-west of
the island of Mangaia.*
*† Tuanaki must have sunk in a marine earthquake in late 1842/early 1843,
for in June 1843 missionaries could no longer locate the island. Not until
1875 was the atoll erased from all maps.*

It was on a bright, perfectly windless April day exactly seven years
ago that I discovered, on a globe in the map department of the
National Library, an island by the name of Ganges that I had
never heard of. The solitary isle was located in the empty expanse
of the north-eastern Pacific Ocean, in the wash of the mighty
Kuroshio, that blue-black rippling ocean current that sweeps
great bodies of warm salty water tirelessly northwards from the
island of Formosa along the Japanese archipelago, and formed
the imaginary northern vanishing point of the Mariana and
Hawaiian Island chains, the latter of which still bore the name
of John Montagu, the Fourth Earl of Sandwich, at least on that
sphere of plaster and elaborately printed papier mâché roughly
the size of a child's head. Intrigued by the familiar name and
unusual position, I embarked on a bit of research which revealed
that, close to the coordinates 31°N 154°E, there had been two
sightings of a coral reef and no less than four sightings of land.
Its existence, however, was repeatedly called into question by

various authorities until, on June 27, 1933, a posse of Japanese hydrographers, after a thorough search of the region in question, announced the official disappearance of Ganges, though the world at large paid little attention to this loss.

Indeed, old atlases record scores of phantom islands. The more accurate the maps became and the less scope they left for uncharted territory, the more frequently seafarers claimed to have sighted such islands, excited by the latest white dots, inspired by the desolation of the fathomless sea, fooled by low-hanging clouds or drifting icebergs, nauseated by briny drinking water, maggoty bread and stringy salt meat, thirsting so eagerly for land and fame that, in their boundless greed, everything they desired coalesced into a cluster of gold and glory, tempting them to note wondrous names in their logbooks alongside prosaic coordinates, to cut through the monotony of their days with would-be discoveries. And so names like Nimrod, Matador and the Auroras started to appear on charts in bold cursive lettering next to the sketchily defined outlines of scattered chunks of land.

Yet it was not these long-unchallenged claims that piqued my interest, but the islands whose one-time existence and subsequent disappearance are vouched for in numerous accounts, and especially the testimonies referring to the sunken isle of Tuanaki, owing in some part, no doubt, to its sonorous name, which has the ring of a long-lost magic word, but above all to the strange reports about the inhabitants of this island stating that fighting was entirely unknown to them and the word "war" was not familiar to them in any of its unpleasant shades of meaning, something that, out of some deep-seated remnant of childlike hope, I was immediately disposed to believe, even if at the same time it reminded me of the wishful utopian dreams outlined in countless treatises which went so far as to claim that another world was possible, but that — as the often verbose descriptions of their increasingly elaborate and hence inhospitable social systems went to show – it was generally only preferable to the existing world in theory. So against my better judgment, I, like so many before me, set out on a search for a land that knew no memory, but only the present, a land in which violence, hardship and death were forgotten, being unknown. And so Tuanaki appeared before me – every bit as magnificent as the sources suggest: an atoll of three islands rising only slightly above sea level in the shallow milky-blue waters of a shimmering lagoon teeming with fish, protected from pounding breakers and relentless tides by a coral reef, home to slender skyward-reaching coconut palms and lush fruit trees, inhabited by a peace-loving people of unrivalled friendliness, in short, a delightful place which, for simplicity's sake, I pictured in my mind's eye as paradise, differentiated from that much-vaunted archetype only by the subtle yet significant fact that no knowledge whatsoever was contained within the fruits of its trees besides that truism that it was more of a blessing to stay here than to go, for, as I soon discovered to my astonishment, in this part of the world the Garden of Eden was held to be a place of refuge rather than one of banishment.

The reports describing this improbable patch of land were just detailed enough to plausibly prove that it did indeed once exist, even if the chronometer never determined its exact position, for neither Tasman nor Wallis, neither Bougainville nor even a captain of some wayward whaling ship ever sighted its gentle shores. Again and again I studied the routes of the major South Sea expeditions, followed the dashed and dotted lines across the graticule and through the paper ocean, and compared them with the presumed position of that island which, in a rush of imperial sentiment, I had marked in the bottom-most empty square.

There was no doubt about it: the explorer celebrated to this day by a small continent as the greatest of all its many seafarers to have criss-crossed the globe, must have only narrowly missed Tuanaki on his third and final voyage. Indeed it must have been only just out of sight when his two vessels, launched originally as colliers in the Whitby fog, passed by it on March 27, 1777 – with sails billowing, proud as frigates, in full regalia. It was more than a month since James Cook's long-serving flagship *Resolution* and her newer, more manoeuvrable consort ship *Discovery* had weighed anchors in their customary bay in Queen Charlotte Sound, New Zealand, as a slight breeze blew up, and travelled through the strait named after their captain, after two days finally leaving behind them the hills of Port Palliser, which shimmered blackish-green in the mist, and heading out to the open sea. But the winds were not in their favour. Fresh, changeable breezes were followed by miserable windless spells, and rain-swept squalls by torturous lulls. Even the drift of the westerly winds, which should have carried them with familiar constancy north-east into the same circle of longitude as Otahaiti, failed – contrary to all seasonal forecasts – to materialise, leaving an ever more worrying distance between them and the next anchorage. A lot of time had already been wasted. And with every passing day, hope faded further of still being able to sail along the coast of New Albion during the approaching northern summer in search of the entrance to that much-attested passage which, on the incomplete charts, promised the long-awaited shortening of the maritime route between the Pacific and Atlantic oceans. For the dream of that corridor, fringed with pack-ice yet still navigable, was old and stubborn like all cosmographers' dreams and had become all the more pressing since the vision of a vast southern continent had had to be abandoned after Cook, in his quest for this legendary land, had ploughed the southern seas in huge, sweeping zigzags and discovered nothing but mountains of ice.

So the two ships drifted along with limp sails, and that

booming silence began to settle on them, so fundamentally different from the peaceful hush of my library existence. Sometimes, though, I could hear the rolling, long-drawn-out ground swell, the taunting of the fine weather, the endless litany of waves forever welling up and subsiding that once seduced Magellan into describing this ocean as the "peaceful" one, a ghostly harmony, the remorseless sound of eternity, more terrifying than the most violent storm, which at least is bound to blow over in time.

Yet this ocean was neither peaceful nor placid, for in its darkest depths lurked indomitable forces that were certain to return. Its seabed was fissured and furrowed, the earth's crust riven with submarine trenches and peaks, unhealed scars from that prehistoric age when the as yet undivided continents, adrift as a single mass in the global ocean, were torn asunder by colossal forces and rammed up against the earth's mantle until their plates were forced, some over, some under each other, down into plunging abysses, up into clear daylight, surrendered to the laws of nature, which know neither mercy nor justice. Water submerged the volcanic cones, and myriads of corals colonised the rims of their craters, building reefs in the light of the sun, the skeletons of new atolls, on whose fertile floors the seeds carried by washed-up branches flourished, while the extinct volcanoes sank down to the dark seabed far below – on the timescale of infinity. And in the midst of this even now still inaudible din, below decks the livestock – the bull, the cows, their calves, the rams, ewes and goats – bleated and lowed with hunger, while the stallion and the mares whinnied, the peacock and his hens screeched and the poultry clucked. Never before had Cook carried so many animals on board, but on this voyage, at the king's express wish, he had brought along half an ark which, like the menagerie of the original model, was assembled with reproduction in mind, and he wondered how Noah had contrived to feed all the hungry mouths, which devoured as much in the way of provisions as an entire ship's company.

On the fifteenth day on the open sea, way off their intended course, the captain, who, as the ship's cooper records in his journal, was particularly concerned about the welfare of the horses, gave the order for eight sheep that were supposed to have populated a South Sea island with their kind to be slaughtered in order to save on hay, supplies of which were steadily dwindling. But some of the meat disappeared from the mess even before it could be prepared, a petty act of theft that had been repeated once too often. The captain sensed insubordination, he sensed betrayal and even — as he docked the meat ration for the entire crew until the culprit was turned in, at which the men refused to touch even that meagre meal — mutiny. The word, an unlit match under the scorching sun, its sole purpose to ignite sparks, hung in the air for a few interminable days during which the wind veered around once more, now blowing from a southerly direction, and seemed to tip the commander from his characteristic aloofness into pure rage. Cook stamped and ranted, a tall, lonely figure, and his curses resounded all the way down to the munitions store. Suspicion rather than worry was now gnawing at his heart, and the image many of the men had of him as a strict but fair father-figure darkened during those days to that of an ageing despot, as unpredictable as the winds. Anyone so inclined may see in the disquieting events of that passage, and in the fact that Cook himself made not a single mention of these episodes in his diary, the seeds of that chain of events which, two years later in a bay on Owyhee, would put a violent end to his life.

But for now the remaining days of a month that seemed to go on interminably ticked by, a month in which time had long since transformed itself into that eternity verging on standstill, in which a single hour and a single day no longer counted for anything. Albatrosses and petrels circled the ships, flying fish flitted through the dry air, porpoises and dolphins swam past, as did a swarm of tiny globular jellyfish about the size of musket balls. Once a large white bird with a red tail appeared, promising land nearby though none could be made out, and on another occasion a thick tree trunk, which had been floating in the water for so long that it was covered in a pale layer of barnacles resembling oozing pus.

Then finally, at 10.00 a.m. on March 29, 1777, the *Discovery*, travelling ahead on the leeward side, hoisted the red, white and blue flag of Holland, the signal for a sighting of land. At almost the same moment the grey-blue shimmering coast became visible on the north-eastern horizon from the masthead of the *Resolution* as well, barely more real than a mirage. The ships headed for the unknown strip of land twinkling in the distance until the sun went down, and tacked all night until the break of day, approaching to within a distance of about four miles of the island, whose south side must have presented an almost painfully enchanting image in the light of the sun as it rose out of the water. Profoundly moved by the heavenly sight, several of the crew members immediately took up quills and brushes, using watery colours and brushstrokes displaying varying degrees of skill to capture the auspicious panorama somewhere other than in unreliable memory: the hills of moderate height shimmering purple in the morning sun, their wooded summits with their many-hued trees and scattered palm crowns, the lush dense green vegetation of the hillsides, the coconuts, breadfruit and plantain visible through the bluish-pink haze.

I studied those pictures, which still conveyed a sense of the longing that had inspired them, in a stuffy room in the cartography department, whose milky windows, as I discovered on enquiry, could not be opened as the pictures had to be protected.

Among the sketches was also the chart drawn by the *Discovery*'s navigator, to whom the task had fallen of recording the dimensions of the island and sketching its cartographic outlines insofar as was possible from the sloop in which he circumnavigated the modestly sized land. The sheet showing the island, whose peaks, indicated with bold strokes, might just as easily have been a whorl of hair on a person's head, was framed with a double line and headed with a doubly absurd name, the chancery script solemnly labelling this as a depiction of "Discovery's Island". One more name, I thought, one more untenable assertion, as presumptuous and vain as the age-old custom that gave rise to it.

For gathered for some time now on the beach were the people who, though they did not realise it themselves, had been discovered and were to be assigned the role – essential for the purpose of any report from far-off lands – of the Natives. Accordingly, the islanders had already taken up position, clubs on shoulders, spears at the ready, and the more of them emerged from the shade of the wooded embankment into the morning light, the louder and more urgent their guttural singing grew. They swung their weapons, hoisted them in the air over and over in time with their shouts – whether with threatening or welcoming intent it was impossible to say, even after much peering through the telescope. For although the crowd of now some two hundred was brought markedly closer by the eyepiece, the wood, brass and glass instrument proved useless for clarifying any matters of real consequence. Despite the genuine curiosity, despite the eloquent descriptions of their language and gestures, physique and clothing, even down to the way they wore their hair and the decoration on their skin, and despite the undeniable precision with which this tribe could then be compared with others in these respects, their view of these people, formed before a single word had been uttered, missed all that was truly of the essence, since it recognised only foreign versus familiar, similar versus different, since it separated that which was one and the same and drew boundaries where there were none, like the overly distinct ragged coastlines on the nautical charts which purported to know where the water ends and the land begins.

I spent a long time thinking about who is truly capable of interpreting signs, the language of muskets and swivel guns, the numerous right and left hands, be they raised or extended, the wild or controlled behaviour, the skewered limbs over an open fire, the touching of nose against nose, a vertically held banana or laurel branch, gestures of greeting, symbols of concord, of canni-balism. What was peace and what was war, what was a beginning and what was an end, what was mercy and what was guile, I wondered as I slumped down on one of the dark-red velvet-upholstered seats in the cafeteria, and observed the people around me preoccupied with their food. The sharing of the same food, the nightly sitting together in the glow of a fire, the exchanging of a thirst-quenching coconut for ironwork and trinkets?

So people stood on the shore, teetered through the shallow water, and reportedly waded out to the reef, dancing and with shrill cries. But what was going through their minds? Who was I to decide that? At the time, although I had no shortage of invita-tions from abroad, I was leading the life of a home-dweller, of a library frequenter, permanently on the lookout for new research subjects to shed light on some hidden source of my existence and lend some kind of meaning to my life by the semblance of a regular daily work routine. So once again: they thought what they thought, and they saw what they saw, and they were right.

This much, though, is as good as certain: that two islanders paddled out to the ships in a canoe with a high, forked stern and did not touch a single one of the gifts tossed in their direction, neither the nails, nor the glass beads nor the shirt of red cloth

either. It is also established that one of them was fearless enough
to take hold of the rope ladder and climb aboard the *Resolution*,
where he introduced himself as Mourua of the island of Mangaia.
He and the captain must have stood facing one another in his
cabin for a while, eye to eye, appraising each other, like two
animals encountering each other for the first time: two men, the
smooth round skull of Mourua versus Cook's birdlike head;
the mild facial features, bright eyes and full lips of the one, the
austere countenance, with a strong nose, thin lips and penetrating
deep-set eyes, of the other; the long black hair bound into a
thick bunch on the crown of the head, the already sparse hair
concealed beneath a silvery-grey wig; the olive skin marked with
black tattoos from shoulder to elbow, next to the pale skin; the
knee-length, ivory-coloured garment fashioned from bast fibres
on the stout, well-fed body, the light-coloured breeches paired
with the open, gold-braided uniform jacket of navy-blue cloth
on the tall, angular figure. Yet the huge scars that disfigured both
men seemed to me like a sign of secret affinity, even if the numerous paintings and prints depicting Cook, and the portrait of
Mourua produced by the ship's artist that afternoon, have the
good grace to omit them: the long, poorly healed wound on
Mourua's forehead, acquired in fighting, and the bulging burn
scar running from between Cook's right thumb and index finger
to his wrist. And as if to seal this moment of unexpected close-
ness, an iron axe was handed over, and the Mangaian took it with
him when he was ferried back to shore in one of the ship's boats.
The surf was still as rough as ever, and soon all hope of mooring
or anchoring was abandoned, for no matter where the plumb
line was dropped, it always indicated that the seabed lay too deep
and moreover was encrusted with sharp coral. And so the ship's
company was beset by a sense of sorrowful regret at having to
leave the island without setting foot on it, a feeling that turned

to agonising disappointment when, in the evening hours, gentle drifts of ambrosial scents were carried over to them on the breeze.

And it was here that I was abandoned by the eyewitness accounts which, though inviting contradiction, had nevertheless brought me to this point, under the English red ensign on board those blue and yellow ships that would recede into the distance at daybreak the following day. I suddenly found myself all alone on deck, or rather on the shore of an island known to me only from a rough outline on a map, and for a moment I forgot that it was not Tuanaki, but its neighbour Mangaia on which I had been cast up, a rayfish-shaped atoll standing five kilometres above the ocean floor, encircled by a broad calcium carbonate reef with numerous inner cliffs and excavations made by the beating of the waves, while in the interior, an undulating landscape of damp peaks with dry flanks on the leeward side overlooked unculti-vated land and swampy lakes. Mangaia's own sources also proved eloquent. They detailed who was or became the son of whom, and who had inherited or snatched what title from whom, ever since the days when their forefathers had paddled out eastwards in logboats and canoes, guided by the Dog Star, and settled on these scattered patches of land. But those stories, rather than fol-lowing the flow of time, traced the paths of blood, which fanned out into different branches and lines of descent, before being repeatedly spilled on the battlefield.

So I could only conjecture as to how Mourua was received on his return to shore, though, for some probably dubious reason, I had a precise picture in my mind of how his fellow islanders pressed him with questions about the nature and provenance of the pale visitors and came to the unanimous conclusion that they had been sent by Tangaroa, the god once worshipped on Mangaia, who, aeons ago, had been defeated in battle by his brother Rongo and had fled out to sea. And I saw in my mind's eye how, recalling that fateful combat, they made their way together to the stone statue of Rongo a little way inland and gave thanks to him for having put the enemy and his followers to flight one more time. In my feeble imagination it was Mourua who stepped before the idol first and launched into the song of praise with the pride of an honourable man whose powerful physique revealed the veteran warrior. A long time had passed since, as an uncircumcised youth armed with an ironwood club, he had joined the back row of combatants, before working his way forward, battle by battle, fearlessly filling the gaps left by his forebears, and had exchanged his weapon for axes and chiselled basalt spearheads. It was on the ground of the old lagoon, windswept cliffs towering over it like the terraces of a huge amphitheatre, that the battle had played out again and again through the ages between the warriors of different clans, the descendants of hostile gods, continuing until the hollow sound of the war drum signalled the battle's end, and the dancing began, its shrill sounds drowning out the groans of the dying, a blood-curdling victory chant that reverberated through the night, superseded only as dawn was breaking by the beat of the peace drum. As his prize, the victor could claim the ruler's title "Mangaia", no less. Mangaia meant peace, Mangaia meant power, a temporary power that was nevertheless solid enough to allow the titleholder to rule on everything: who was allowed to cultivate and live on which patch of land, and who would be banished to the barren, karstic rocky reef where nothing prospered but dry foliage. It was not uncommon for the losers to remain there in the clammy limestone caves until they were nothing but skin and bone – or had reproduced in such numbers that they were hopeful of winning victory over their one-time conquerors in the next battle. I saw the whites of their eyes flashing in the semi-darkness, heard the water dripping from the stalactites onto their heads and necks, tasted the musty air.

Power, as I discovered during those weeks in which the rites and customs of that island were revealed to me in the ethnological reports of the first missionaries, was not passed down through the generations on Mangaia, but won – seized in battle or snatched in a night-time spree that, more often than not, degenerated into a massacre in which the betrayed, anaesthetised with ground kava root, were dumped in a pit, covered in hot stones and left to stew in their own juices until they were fit to eat.

Now, though, Mourua's hands clasped the strangely gleaming axe, and anyone regarding it as nothing but a lump of iron on a wooden shaft, a well-meant gift, fails to do justice to its power. From then on, this axe was conferred upon whoever emerged victorious on Mangaia, since it was more useful than any other tool, allowing wood to be split with the same ease as the skull of a doomed man on Rongo's altar at the start of the reign of each new ruler.

Mangaia was not just one island among countless thousands in this fathomless ocean but a whole world in itself, in which it made no difference whether you were condemned to starve to death in the labyrinth of mouldy grottos or to perish in a rotten pirogue under the scorching sun. The loser forfeited everything, his name, his land, his life, and those who contrived to save themselves harboured no thought of returning. Some managed to escape, and evidence suggests that those lucky few found refuge on the island of Tuanaki, two days' voyage away. On Mangaia, though, one ruler followed another until the cycle of victory and defeat was brought to an abrupt end. It's the same old story, in its various versions: strangers came, invaders who needed to be repelled, whalers bearing a mottled seashell in their chapped hands, its toothed opening like a hungry mouth; missionaries and their wives who, barely had they reached the shore, cast themselves back into the surf in mortal fear, leaving all their worldly goods behind on the beach: a boar and a sow, which henceforth, dressed in bast, would be revered as a pair of divinities, thick books filled with black characters resembling tattoos, whose torn-out, wafer-thin pages made a rustling adornment for the dancers, and lastly an unnamed plague that claimed more victims than all the battles put together. That was the beginning – and what then followed was the end, a long process of parting company with the gods. Their ironwood images were stripped bare, their sacred groves desecrated, their shrines burned down. The protests of the last pagan tribe went as unheeded as their pleas for mercy in the final battle. Those who would not be converted were killed with axes made of American steel, and from the rubble of the Rongo statue soon a church was built. Cook's axe was now no more than a rusty relic of past times and past rulers which, now that it had served its purpose, was presented to a second-generation English missionary, whether with pride or in the vague hope of thereby strengthening or rupturing the bond once forged I could not discover. Since it was not clear to the missionary either, he promptly dispatched the lump of iron to the British Museum.

I found myself thinking about the forces in the Earth's interior. Wherever they prevail, the age-old cycle of rise and fall, blossom and decay is cut short. Islands emerge and are submerged. They have a shorter lifespan than the lands of the continent; they are temporary phenomena – compared to the lifetime, running into millions of years, and the endless expanse of this ocean represented in turquoise, azure or light blue on the reverse sides of all the globes on display in the cartography department, which I now ceremoniously patrolled, convinced I had finally found the thread, the thin umbilical cord binding Mangaia and Tuanaki together: it was the might of a marine earthquake that one day lifted Mangaia up from the seabed and out of the water, a ring of dead coral and basalt lava, a mountain summit rising steeply out of the depths. And it was the might of a marine earthquake that one day dragged Tuanaki down into the depths and submerged it beneath the water masses of the Pacific Ocean, not long after missionaries had started looking for the atoll. The grey shadow of a giant wave must have approached from the horizon almost without a sound and engulfed everything in one go. The next day, so I imagined, there was nothing in the place where the island had been but dead trees floating on the glassy surface of the ocean.

Only a year earlier, a small schooner with a crew of seven had found the entrance to the reef and made it to the deserted shores of Tuanaki. One of the sailors, at the behest of the captain, had set off, armed only with a sword, towards the interior of the island, made his way through the jungle of banana trees, coconut palms, bougainvillea and wild orchids, breathed in the air perfumed with frangipani, hibiscus and white jasmine, and finally discovered, in a clearing, a meeting house in which a number of men were gathered. All of them, I read with endless satisfaction in the one and only report describing that encounter, wore the Mangaian poncho and spoke the Mangaian dialect.

One of them, no doubt the eldest, motioned to the visitor to enter, and when he complied, the old man enquired as to the whereabouts of the ship's captain.

"He's in the boat," the sailor replied truthfully.

"Why doesn't he come inland?" the man asked, without altering his expression. A shell horn dangled from his neck.

"He is afraid you might kill him."

Silence fell, and for a brief moment the breakers seemed ominously close. The old man gazed at the forest foliage. At last he said, with utter calm: "We don't know how to fight. We only know how to dance."

My gaze alighted on the pale-blue globe one last time. I soon found the location. Right there, to the south of the equator, between a few scattered islands, this perfect patch of land had stood, remote from the world, having forgotten everything it had ever known about it. The world, though, only grieves for what it knows, and has no inkling of what it lost with that tiny islet, even though, given the spherical form of the Earth, this vanished dot could just as easily have been its navel, even if it was not the sturdy ropes of war and commerce that bound them one to the other, but the incomparably finer-spun thread of a dream. For myth is the highest of all realities and – so it struck me – the library the true theatre of world events.

Outside, rain had set in, a damp monsoon, unusually warm for these northern latitudes.

Ancient Rome
CASPIAN TIGER
Panthera tigris virgata, also known as *Persian*, *Mazandaran*,
Hyrcanian and *Turanian tiger*

* *It was the separation of their territories, less than ten thousand years ago, that led
to the split into two subspecies, the Siberian and the Caspian tiger. The Caspian
tiger lived in the upper reaches of the River Aras, from the forested slopes and
plains of the Talysh mountain range to the Lankaran lowlands, on the southern
and eastern shores of the Caspian Sea, on the northern side of the Alborz
mountain range up to the River Atrek, in the southern part of the Kopet Dag
mountain range as far as the Murgab River basin, as well as along the upper
stretch of the Amu Darya and its tributaries, in the Amu Darya valley to the
point where it reaches the Aral Sea, and in the lower reaches of the Zeravshan,
upstream of the Ili, along the River Tekes and into the Taklamakan desert.*
† *Direct hunting, a dwindling habitat and a decline in its main prey populations were the reasons for the extinction of the Caspian tiger. One was shot
in 1954 in the Sumbar River valley in the Kopet Dag range, on the Iran-
Turkmenia border. Other reports suggest the last tiger was killed in 1959 in the
Golestan National Park in northern Iran. Caspian tigers were last sighted
in 1964 in the foothills of the Talysh mountains and the river basin of the
Lankaran lowlands near the Caspian Sea. In the early 1970s, biologists from
the Iranian Department of Environment spent years scouring the remote,
uninhabited Caspian forests for them, in vain. None survived in captivity.
A handful of preserved cadavers found their way into natural history collections in London, Tehran, Baku, Almaty, Novosibirsk, Moscow and St
Petersburg. A stuffed Caspian tiger was on display in the Tashkent Museum
of Natural History until the mid-1960s, when it was destroyed in a fire.*

In the evening they are hungry and restless. No meat for days. No hunting since they themselves were captured. Instincts worn down by captivity until they lie bare like gnawed bones. Fire blazes in the cats' eyes. It is the reflection of the torches. These herald the arrival of the handlers who, each time they pass by on their rounds, peer through the bars, listen into the darkness for signs that their cargo is still alive.

The cage opens. Yet rather than a meal, it is a den that awaits them. Torches guide the way. Spears force them into a black, windowless hole, two wooden crates barely higher than their withers. These are rolled onto the waiting wagons. Senses sharpened by hunger. Commotion, movement, a clamour of voices: the barked orders of the handlers, the piercing whistle of the driver, the jangling of the bridles, the clunking of the corn barges against a far-off quay, the clatter of the wheels, the flick of a rope.

The convoy jerks into motion, sets out on its preordained path. To the innermost heart of the city. To the outermost reaches of being. The axles creak at every turn.

The two animals are separated by a single partition. They crouch in the darkness. They know everything and see nothing. Not the mouldering docks and the steaming knacker's yard, not the Praenestine Gate, which they pass, not the buildings of marble and Tiburtine stone that gleam even at night. They are animals. Animals like us. Doomed like us.

It is still night when they are taken into the catacombs. During the last hours of darkness they turn in tight, aimless circles, strangers to one another – whether equally matched remains to be seen. The cells are musty; dungeons hidden from the sun. And when it finally rises, not one ray filters down here, into this underworld of passageways, ramps and lifts, of traps and doors.

Far above them a sail is now unfurled until it arches like a second sky over the stone bowl that is gradually filling with people:

consuls and senators, vestal virgins and knights, citizens and freedmen, discharged legionaries – and at the very top, around the edge, the women. They have all come to see. They have come to be seen. It is a feast day, a spectacle, and anyone calling it a game has failed to appreciate the holy order inherent in it and the deadly seriousness that attends it.

The day is still young as the emperor steps into his box, pushes back the hood of his robe, shows off his tall sturdy physique, his stout neck, his imposing profile that everyone knows from the coins. When finally he sits down, the dungeon is unlocked, a chasm opens at ground level and a colossal animal of a kind never before seen emerges from the pit, bursts into the ring, races around the enclosure, leaps high against the parapet separating the public from the arena and, with a thunderous din, beats its mighty paws against the iron gate, stops, looks around, and for an infinite moment stands still.

This beast is preceded by a reputation that transcends oceans and mountains: it is said to originate from the depths of the forests of Hyrcania, the wild, rugged, evergreen land that borders the Caspian Sea. Its name is at once a curse and an incantation. It is reputed to be swift as an arrow, wild as the Tigris, the fastest-flowing of all rivers, from which it takes its name. Its fur blazes red as an open fire, the sooty stripes akin to branches in the embers, the facial features finely drawn, the ears upstanding, the cheeks powerful, the muzzle bristling with white whiskers, the eyes glowing green beneath heavy brows, and on its forehead a dark symmetrical marking, the meaning of which no-one knows.

The creature shakes its huge head, reveals its large, terrible teeth, its two pointed fangs, its fleshy maw. It runs its tongue over its bare nose. A growl rises up from its throat; a hoarse snarl unlike anything heard before echoes through the terraces – a blood-curdling sound, after which every word becomes a whisper.

And a rumour circulates, half lore, half poem: that there exist only females of its species, for the animal is savage, as savage as only a mother can be when robbed of her offspring. Chance alone bears out the assertion: beneath the tail with its brown-black rings lies concealed a fertile womb that will bear no more cubs.

The animal moves off again, paces the ring with silent steps, clings to the shadow cast by the walls, looks for a spot offering refuge, quiet and shelter – and finds none. There is only the greasy grey of the palisade, the barred openings, the white dazzle of the billowing togas, patches of brightness, naked faces frozen into masks.

When, in fact, had they first set eyes on this animal? Not in a nightmare, as a man-eating manticore with the sneering face of a child, its bared jaws full of powerful teeth, its tail armed with stings, but in the flesh, part of an Indian delegation on the shores of the island of Samos. On that occasion too it had been a female, the only one of the group of solitary beasts to have survived the desperately long, torturous journey. It was paraded before Augustus on a wrought-iron chain as a gesture of reverence – and as a hideous wonder of nature, as rare and horrifying as the herm-like boy who had been made to stand beside it: half-naked, his whole body dusted with spices, with no arms, these having been cut off at the shoulders when he was still an infant. There they stood, the snarling animal and the mutilated human – two wondrous beings, a bizarre pair, a cue for poets to pen epigrams about the majesty of the abominable.

It was six years later that this creature was first seen in Rome. On the Nones of May, it was paraded at the long-awaited inauguration of this theatre, together with a rhinoceros and a patterned snake ten cubits in length. The beast was changed beyond all recognition, for it could be seen licking its handler's hands with its rough tongue like a dog.

The empire of the Romans was vast, extending raggedly in every direction under the sun. Not only had they subjugated the Latins, the Volsci, the Aequi, the Sabines and Etruscans, they had also conquered the Macedonians, the Carthaginians and Phrygians, even claimed victory over the Syrians and Cantabrians – and had now tamed this monster as they would a barbarian people, driving out its wild nature with whips and crowbars, winning its trust with goat and rabbit meat, and in return granting it protection, as they did all their subjects. It seemed almost as though this tigress, who blinked away every ray of sunshine yet did not flinch from the intrusive glances of the humans, were about to be declared a citizen of this empire, like a slave about to be set free. But then from somewhere, more out of whim than conviction, came the call for revenge, which never fails to resonate, the unchanging shrill chorus of budding suspicion and sudden distrust. It was suspected that their submission was merely feigned, their gentleness but a ruse. The predator may have hidden its claws, rolled on its back and, with its belly fur exposed, asked the handler for a caress, yet it lost none of its terror. Almost nothing stokes fear as surely as having won power over an enemy to whom one still feels inferior despite the victory. For as always, there was no denying the truth: nature was not vanquished, the wild remained untamed. Every breath the animal took served as a reminder of long-held fears and impending doom – and rendered its swift death as necessary as the sacrifice of thanksgiving after victory in battle. The verdict was unanimous: the tame beast was to die in combat, like all enemies of Rome. Yet when they set about choosing an adversary, no-one could be found who dared to take up the challenge. So they killed it in its cage.

Chains rattle, swords clatter, a wooden hatch drops onto the sand. The ground opens. A murmur passes through the tiers. Out of the darkness a tan head appears. A lion steps into the arena, calm, composed, his head held high, framed by the cloak of his rusty-black mane. The dark wool extends down over his shoulders to his underbelly, a shaggy coat. He sees the unfamiliar feline, takes in her perfect predator's build. The two animals stand there and eye each other for the first time — from a safe distance. Beyond the gates, a horse whinnies, a whip cracks. Otherwise all is quiet. Everyone is leaning forward to try and interpret the beasts' expressions, their mute demeanour, their motionless stance. But nothing gives them away. No hint of superiority, nor any trace of that understanding that binds predator and prey out in the wild.

The lion now sits, enthroned, showing no sign of agitation, with his shoulders drawn in and his chest proud, rigid as a statue, a long-serving monarch. No-one can say which came first: his noble status or his heroic appearance. A world that does not venerate him is unthinkable. A fable that does not make him the ruler not worth telling. His mane shimmers reddish in the sunlight. His gaze is frozen. His eyes gleam amber. The furry tassel of his tail whips the grainy dry sand. He opens his jaws, wider and wider, reveals his big yellow teeth, pushes his head forward, pricks back his ears, narrows his eyes to a thin slit — and starts to roar, a groan issuing from the depths of his chest, again and again, followed by a terrible rumble that seems to rise from an even deeper abyss each time, growing ever louder and more breathless, ever more urgent and menacing. It is the howl of a raging tempest, say the Indians, the roar of a charging army, the Egyptians, the thunder of Jehovah's fury, the Hebrews. But it might also be the elemental sound of creation announcing the end of the world.

The tigress drops low, tenses her long narrow body like a bowstring, presses her straggly white beard into the sand, stretches her hind legs in feline fashion, the sheer power of her muscles smouldering beneath her shoulders. With infinite caution she advances one paw, then the next, creeps and sidles closer and closer, pauses — the lion in her sights.

He sees her coming, but remains calm. The lion's proverbial bravery is borne out. Fear has no hold over him. He stays stock-still on his spot and awaits whatever may come. Only his tail swishes back and forth, describing the same curves over and over in the dust. Destruction blazes in his eyes. And perhaps there is truth in what is written: that his blood is hot enough to melt diamonds.

There comes a breeze; a pigeon is briefly trapped beneath the sail and flutters in search of open sky. In this instant the tigress launches herself, springs through the air at the lion. He rears up, the two animals collide with a dull thud, and a tangle of bodies and fur writhes in the sand, turning lightning pirouettes until flashes of bare wooden boards show through. A hissing, panting and roaring fills the theatre, mingles with choruses of hooting and bawling, swells to a deafening racket that embodies everything: the plaintive cries of an exhausted lion in a dark pit, the hoarse yelps of a tiger cub caught in a net, the weary trumpeting of a wounded elephant, the groans of a hind pursued to the point of exhaustion, the pitiful squeals of an injured pregnant sow.

They come from the furthest reaches of the empire; panthers, lions and leopards from Mauritania, Nubia and the Gaetulian forests, crocodiles from Egypt, elephants from India, wild boar from the banks of the Rhine and elk from the Nordic swamps. They come in ships with sails and oars, in torrential rain, heat and hailstorms, wretched from the swell of the sea, with bloodied paws and teeth filed blunt, in crates of rough elm and beech wood, like prisoners of war or condemned criminals, on some ponderous conveyance drawn by oxen which, when they turn their bowed necks beneath the yoke and catch sight of their cargo, immediately shrink back from the drawbar, snorting, their eyeballs white with terror.

Under towering skies the wagons cross the shimmering plains and dark forests, the barren or fertile terrain, stop and rest in the shabbiest parts of towns and villages, which are required by law to provide for the animals and their keepers. All this for Rome, that temporary, fragile centre of an empire that nourishes itself from its peripheries. But most die along the way. Carcasses thrown overboard, bloated by the water, dried out by the sun, a meal for dogs and vultures. Theirs is a cruel fate, though it seems kinder than that of the survivors.

They roll into Rome on high-wheeled wagons alongside the military equipment, receiving an enthusiastic welcome like all rare and precious goods, their names and places of capture emblazoned in large lettering.

They are kept outside the city walls, near the docks, crammed into cages, prepared for the arena where every hunter becomes prey, and those found stoical are stirred to hatred. If an animal is overly docile, it is left to starve for days on end, pelted with sharp thorns and burning brushwood, festooned with bits of jangling metal or teased with straw dolls dressed in red. Any animal that refuses to fight in the amphitheatre, that is reluctant to play the role assigned to it by others, has lost its life. The games are serious. As serious as the deaths of those men and women whose memory they honour: victorious generals, heirs of Caesar who perished before their time, the emperor's father and mother.

The fight is sacred. To force the spectacle, tormentor-slaves chain the animals to one another: aurochs to elephants, rhinoceroses to bulls, ostriches to boars, lions to tigers, so that animals that would never come across each other out in the wild face each other in the semicircle of the arena – forced into hostility, robbed of their habitat, driven to a state of terror and frenzy, exposed to everyone's gaze, tethered to existence by invisible cords, condemned to die the painful and entertaining death for which they have been kept alive. The verdict may be unequivocal, but the crime of which they are guilty remains obscure to the last.

It may be an old ritual, but here no-one pulls their toga over their head to spare themselves the sight of death. No god will be appeased by these steaming entrails. No dirge will extol these dead, no cenotaph will conceal their corpses, and only those that survive countless games, cheating death again and again, those that kill even the *bestiarii* and remain alone in the arena at the end earn themselves a posthumous reputation and a name: the she-bear Innocentia and the lion Cero II, who in the end was savaged by a nameless tiger before a clamouring crowd.

The tigress shakes herself free, rolls to one side. The lion lashes at her with his right paw, catches her on the head, rips a flap of skin from her scalp. He scents blood, he scents the injured kid bleating for its mother that once lured him into the trap in the wastelands of the Atlas mountains, he scents victory and defeat. He hurls himself onto her back with all his might, his hind legs on the ground, buries his claws in her neck, tugs her head backwards. The tigress yelps, hisses, bares her fearful teeth. Again the lion moves to attack, drives the tigress back until her tail is brushing the walls of the arena, pursues her, pounces at her once more, aims for her throat and sinks his teeth into her neck with full force. The battle seems already decided. A soft moan escapes the tigress, like a sigh. A bloody triangular wound gapes beneath her left ear. She ducks, writhes, finally frees herself from his clutches, leaps onto the back of her adversary, buries her paws in his neck, drags him to the ground, digs her claws into his fur, springs apart from him again and lands a distance of two rods

away in the swirling dust. Cheers go up, applause resounds, a
fanfare plays.

The lion, looking dazed, gasps for air, turns his heavy head
and surveys his wounds, two red gashes running across his back.
Then he shakes his mane, reverts to combat stance, charges at
the tigress, groaning, snorting – with a bellow of pain. She lunges
out, aims for his forelegs. The two of them rear up and lash out
at each other. Red, yellow and black fur goes flying. The crowd
yells, erupts into chanting, shouts wild encouragement for the
fight it has contrived. They call it a hunt, but there is no undergrowth, and every way out is blocked by the barricade, the high
walls resembling occupied battlements.

They are watching a cross between an execution and a theatri-
cal performance. A crude throng with refined tastes, accustomed
to the magnitude, the sheer numbers, the monstrosity. To everything the mind can imagine. Every boundary only there to be
overstepped. Their delight is laced with disgust, and their disgust
with delight born purely of curiosity, the urge to act on every
thought. For they, though they pride themselves on having a
choice, are similarly only following their instincts, like children
who throw stones at frogs just for fun.

Curiosity also spawns the question of who would win if all
the animals from the menageries were brought here to test their
powers and penned in together in this sandy abyss. A drama that
simultaneously quells every fear it unleashes. A spectacle, bigger
than the games staged by Augustus to honour his prematurely
deceased heir. What, then, would represent the pinnacle of all
ferocity? A trained tiger that tears apart a tame lion? A lion that
chases rabbits around the arena, scoops them up and carries them
around in its jaws like its own flesh and blood, toys with them
then releases them, only to catch them again? Hecatombs of big
cats being paraded and slaughtered in the arena in a single day

until women faint and the ground is littered with bodies that can no longer be called bodies, lacerated, torn to pieces, drenched in blood, the heads twitching, the carcasses half-eaten, the limbs cold and rigid?

The Circus will be reincarnated. For once a thought comes into the world, it lives on in another. Big cats crouching on pedestals, piled into pyramids, posing in quadrille formation. They will ride on horses, glide on wheels, rock on seesaws, balance on ropes, jump through flaming hoops – use dressed-up dogs as hurdles until the crack of the whip, which is the signal to lick the sandals of the animal trainer dressed in a gladiator tunic and tow him around the ring in the chariot: lion and tigress – the social animal of the steppes, the loner of the damp forests – side by side, an unequal pair yoked together as if pulling Bacchus' chariot as depicted in the mosaics found at ancient sites: Africa versus Asia, control versus passion. What use to them their heroic past, their honourable titles on a par with those of the Caesars? The lion has become the pet of emperors and saints. While he is fulfilling martyrs' deepest desires, others are pillaging his realm. One privilege is gained, another lost. Cities, countries, kings demand his image on their crests. And in assuming this new role, he forgets his origins, the broad plains, the strength of the sun, hunting as a pride. And what use is it now to the tiger that it remained forgotten in Europe for a thousand years? True, its rarity did save it from becoming a frozen emblem. A strange creature classified in Latin bestiaries as either a serpent or a bird, judged by a foreign concept of virtue. They cursed it as cowardly when they should have called it clever. It evaded humans for as long as it could.

Look far into the future, see their sorry fate: their house will fall like that of the Julii, their lineage snuffed out, their last descendants stuffed like bird carcasses. Forever trapped in dioramas with the dusty steppe or broken reeds in the background, hissing, with glassy eyes, mouth open wide, their mighty eye-teeth bared menacingly – or beseechingly, as at the moment of their death. A life in nature reserves and in the custody of humans, behind glass and ditches, among artificial rocks, in tiled rooms and bar-less enclosures, their days sacrificed to inactivity, flies swarming around their heads, an existence marked only by eating and digesting, in the air the smell of mutton, horsemeat, beef, and of warmed-up blood.

The audience rages. The fight ceases abruptly. The animals release their grip on each other, pause, breathing heavily. Blood trickles down their flanks. The tigress drags herself away, leans her broken body against the barricade, struggles for air. The lion stays put, muscles twitching, chaps drenched in blood, mouth brimming with foam. His gaze is dull and empty, his eyes bottomless. His ribcage rises and falls, breathing the dust. A shadow falls across the stage, a cloud obscures the sun, just for a moment.

Then all of a sudden the arena brightens; unfamiliar light illuminates the scene. An opportunity appears, like a miracle, an unimagined glimpse into the future, a way out, a departure from the preordained path, something new and different that banishes any thought of approaching death. Yet it is also the need, the urge to survive that drives the two animals inevitably towards one another in that vision. A force connected not with the end, but with a beginning. Their ritual obeys a powerful age-old rule: safeguard your clan, preserve your species before its line dies out. And when coming into heat, know no choice. If one instinct fails, let another take its place. Whoever lives must eat. Whoever eats must procreate. Whoever procreates will not perish. The signals may encourage hostility, but the message is clear, the musk in their urine an invitation to a game with consequences: menacing gesture is followed by a hint of timidity, proximity by flight, and resistance by sudden, fleeting submission.

They rub up against each other, nuzzle their heads together. They swipe at one another, hesitate, their paws raised, their eyes locked on each other, they fend off the inevitable, flee their beloved foe, stir the embers, feel their fervour build to the point of no return, rapt and mesmerised.

Eventually the orange-and-black cat slumps down, prone, and the lion steps over her, lowers his fawn body, sinks down on her, and while, for all their kinship, a vestige of unfamiliarity remains, the process is well known: he sinks his teeth into her neck with a roar until she lashes out at him, hissing, and – be it with a blind or seeing eye – they mate, driven to it only by their unnatural proximity. Nothing on earth can prevent what is now happening. Who decides what is contrary to nature and what is part of it? What are those cats doing if not heeding the call to be fruitful and multiply? Traitors to their species yet also its preservers. That their nuptials were enforced need not trouble their descendants.

And after a hundred days, what began as a dream reappears like an illusion, a creature resembling a chimaera, in which the parents' nature is both doubled and halved: the tail black, but without a tassel, the belly pale, the mane short and the coat light as sand, a reddish ochre dappled with patches that gleam like stripes, the father's stature, the mother's profile, their un-matched silhouettes, the straight back of the lion, the roach back of the tiger. Monstrous in size, its being intrinsically divided, quick-tempered like a tiger, stoical and tenacious like a lion – a social animal condemned to solitude, a swimmer that shuns water, a popular attraction, a spellbinding sight – bastard, lion-tiger, liger.

They're everywhere, aren't they? In the colour copperplate of the three cubs from the travelling menagerie of an English performer, which were taken from their tiger mother and given to a terrier bitch to nurse, and all perished in their first year of life. In the naively rendered, colourful painting of a hybrid feline family in their enclosure, their trainer in their midst like their own child. In the footage of the sandy-coloured liger beside a lady in a silver bathing costume, a colossal animal, the world's largest cat, a male of keen instinct and lost potency.

A cry resounds around the upper tiers, people wince, momentarily avert their gaze then turn their faces back to the arena. The dream ends abruptly; the offspring remain unborn. And as if to dispel the thought, the spectacle gathers pace. The entire globe and its myriad worlds dwindle to this semicircle, this inhospitable place, the bare enclosure composed of sand, spectators and stone, where flies buzz and some in the crowd fan cool air on themselves with a restless hand.

The tigress picks herself up and circles her adversary again. The embattled lion fends her off, but his blows miss their target. The orange cat draws back and launches into a leap, shoots through the air like a bullet, lands on the lion's back. The huge bodies, now streaked with blood and brown with dust, roll across the arena. The lion gives a hoarse roar, shakes the tigress off, pants, stumbles, sinks to his knees. He has two gaping wounds running across his back; blood streams from deep tooth marks. Immediately the tigress leaps onto his shoulders once more, sinks her fangs into his throat. Only his mane saves him from certain suffocation. The tigress loosens her bite, gasps for air herself, great mouthfuls of lion hair catching in her teeth. At this the lion lunges out, hits her hard. The tigress sways but recovers herself, surges forward anew. They go in for another attack. The tigress throws herself on the lion, sinks her teeth into his flesh. He rears up, shakes her off, opens his mouth wide, collapses on the sand with a fading moan. And lies there, motionless.

The tigress surveys her work, sinks down and, trembling, licks her wounds. The stripes in her fur are barely visible for blood.

Emperor Claudius laughs his loud, depraved laugh. There is spittle clinging to the corners of his mouth. He stands, takes a step forward and starts to speak, keen to praise the mother whose memory today's games are intended to honour.

He stutters, though, and the words disintegrate in his mouth. Mute, he slumps back into his seat, hearing in his head the abominable name his mother once called him: a monster. The vile word echoes inside him, a curse that has haunted him for as long as he can remember. Who could blame her? What then brought him to power? The mere fact that he was alive, the only member of the imperial family, the last of his line. Nobody had ever taken him seriously, him, the monster.

So it was pure chance that bequeathed him the office that was never meant for him: benefactor to the masses, ruler over life and death. He sees the marble seats of the senators, the narrow purple hem of the knights' togas, the quizzical looks. Were it not for the fear, it would be easy to rule. Sweat trickles down his temples.

A bell rings. A gate opens. The crowd yells. A man enters the arena. A *bestiarius*, wearing nothing more than a tunic, no armour nor shield, bandages around his legs, in his left hand a bridle, in his right a spear which he keeps raising aloft, directing the masses. The tigress sees the half-naked figure, stalks him, prepares to pounce – but in that split second the lance pierces her chest. The tigress writhes, staggering blindly, trying to shake off the spear. Her head hangs, her eyes search, incredulous, her gaze moves over the fighter, the spectators, who are in a raging frenzy – and the animal slumps down. Her eyes fade, her gaze freezes. Bright blood flows from her nostrils; red froth streams from her open mouth. Already the *bestiarius* is performing his lap of honour, taking in the applause, the chants, the dancing pennants, the wild behaviour. Duty has been done, order restored, chaos defeated for a moment.

Gradually the grandstand empties. Quiet descends. Men come and drag the carcasses out of the arena, down into the catacombs to join those of the other animals piled there in their hundreds. The odour of decay hangs in the air. In the afternoon comes the main event, the gladiator games.

Valais Alps
GUERICKE'S UNICORN

The physicist Otto von Guericke, who was known principally for his vacuum experiments, is also credited with being the first person to have recreated an animal skeleton from individual finds. In actual fact, Guericke, who in 1672 in his New Magdeburg Experiments *mentioned the discovery of the "skeleton of a unicorn" in 1663 in the gypsum quarries of the Sewecken hills near Quedlinburg, could not have discovered those bones, let alone have reassembled them. Indeed two copperplate engravings dating from 1704 and 1749 suggest they originated from a number of ice-age mammals including the mammoth and the woolly rhinoceros.*
† *The bones in question were initially kept in Quedlinburg Castle, but were later handed out piecemeal to anyone interested.*
A more than three-metre-tall plastic replica of the unicorn skeleton, on permanent loan from the local municipal savings bank, can be seen today in the Museum of Natural History in Madgeburg.

Years ago I spent some time in the mountains. Tired out from a lengthy endeavour, I decided to spend a few weeks staying in a deserted Alpine hamlet in a chalet that an acquaintance had invited me to use. I was toying with the idea, which I had thought original at the time, of writing a guide to monsters, those beasts that, despite having sprung mostly from human imagination, still, as I had once blithely asserted when pitching this book project, in spite of all denials of their existence, populated the world just as surely as all the varieties of real-life fauna, meaning that, as I suggested to the group of potential financial backers, it was possible not only to research but also to categorise their nature, their physical features, their ancestral habitats and individual behaviour. Dragons should not be slain but dissected, I added rather pathetically, and without giving any great thought to my target group, or the size or format of my book, I signed a contract and caught the next night train heading south.

I arrived around midday at the railway station of a little mediaeval town. It was mid-April, the air still chilly, the sun feeble, the onward bus journey seemingly interminable and the footpath from the last bus stop up to the hamlet stony and steep, just as I had imagined the walk to a retreat would be. I remember, as I followed the twists and turns of the bridle path across a rugged expanse of scree, being amused by the thought that I, who as a child had been rather anxious and afraid, especially, of horror films and of being alone, now, in self-imposed isolation, wanted to concern myself with, of all things, the often terrifying monsters born of human imagination. That my climb was so slow and arduous was mainly due, however, to the huge number of books I had packed.

It was not until darkness was beginning to fall that the black and white houses scattered over the mountainside came into view behind a rocky slope. All around was silence. Only the power lines carried by the pylons buzzed above me. I found the key in the agreed hiding place, entered the modest but spacious upstairs living room with its broad larchwood panelling, fetched firewood from the side of the chalet, stacked it next to the stove, lit the fire, brewed myself some tea and made up my bed. It was not long before darkness descended over the mountainside and over my new home, and my sleep on that first night – if my memory serves me well – was deep and dreamless.

When I awoke the next morning, the sky through the roof light looked like a pallid pulp, and it took me a moment to remember where on earth I was. Outside, rising above the shaded, densely wooded valley were jagged, snow-capped summits which, not for lack of trying, I was unable to match up with the names on a map I had found lying ready on the kitchen table. Perhaps it was due to having grown up by the sea, which knows neither elevations nor depressions and remains shapeless even during stormy weather, I thought, as an area of dark hatching indicating a trench projecting laterally into the broad valley basin caught my eye.

I put on my parka, stepped into my walking boots and went out, straight into the wood. Bluetits chirruped, a ring ouzel whistled, lingering patches of snow glistened in hollows, and the trunks of quite a few of the trees were enveloped in a neon-green fluorescent weave of tiny spiky arm-like branches, which further corroborated my observation that even completely artificial-looking organisms occur in nature. It came away easily from the bark and felt like moss in my coat pocket. After half an hour I came to a ravine gaping like a jagged wound in the mountainside. A narrow wooden footbridge of barely a hand's breadth spanned the damp shadowy abyss.

I made an about turn, and the sun had just risen over the eastern ridge when I arrived back at the hamlet. The air was still chilly. I could see my breath, which, along with the smoke from my chalet chimney, was the only sign of human life far and wide. The two dozen houses stood there mute, their living quarters of dark timber set on stone bases, their roof ridges facing the valley, with blank windows and closed shutters, and the door of the chapel on the edge of the village would not open either. In front of it stood a water trough hewn from a boulder. The water was ice-cold.

The first week passed without notable incident: I got up at eight o'clock each day, went for a long walk to the ravine and back before breakfast, and on my return, as if I had done it every day of my life, I threw two or three logs on the fire, brewed coffee, boiled

myself an egg, sat down at the round kitchen table and read. I had
the place to myself and had stocked up with supplies in the first
few days to spare myself the walk to the grocery store in the
village lower down the valley for a time. I had plenty of wood, as
well as books and a document folder full of photocopied psycho-
analytical, medical history, cryptozoological and other fantastical
research literature, and it pleased me to think that, in the event
of the kind of disaster that I fantasised about in recurring day-
dreams, at least there would be enough combustible fuel to last
me a while.

And so I immersed myself in my studies and quickly filled a
whole notebook with details of the diverse features of the monsters and mythical beasts, as well as the legends surrounding
them and the functions each of these creatures performed in the
teeming cosmos of fear. I admit I was a little disappointed. The
similarities were all too obvious: each new story soon turned out
to be an amalgamation of old familiar set-pieces, and each figure
an unsurprising hybrid of the imaginary and the true-to-life. In
short, there was not exactly an abundance of species, indeed real
life was considerably more eccentric than fiction. So all the stories
of monstrous beings testified to little more than the dogged per-
sistence of repeated narrative patterns and motifs: the phoenix
that is consumed by flames every five hundred years only to rise
from its own ashes, the self-important sphinx with its riddles, the
deadly gaze of Medusa, of the catoblepas, of the basilisk. All
the varieties of dragon, which are always slain in the end, their
membranous wings, their breath that befouls the air, their hunger
for gold, the inevitable bloodbath. Even fabulous creatures from
foreign cultures failed to deliver the variety I had hoped for. It
always basically boiled down to the same: a woman's innocence
had to be protected or sacrificed, a man's bravery proved, the wild
tamed, the unfamiliar conquered and the past overcome. What I

particularly disliked about these accounts were the hints at deeper meaning, the grandiose air of the incredible, their inevitable allusion to some calamity either impending or having occurred in the dim and distant past. More wearying still were the conclusions drawn by researchers eager to see these beasts as nothing but a misunderstood reality. For them there was no mystery whatsoever. The dog-headed people, the cynocephalics, were merely a group of marauding baboons, the phoenix a flamingo blurred by the dazzle of the morning sun, the bishop-fish of the historical pamphlets simply stray monk seals, and the unicorn a misinterpreted rhinoceros or an oryx antelope in profile. But, to my disappointment, I was nowhere able to find a convincing answer to the most obvious question of why dragons bore such a striking resemblance to dinosaurs.

Nevertheless, I persisted with my plan and attempted an initial categorisation of the monsters, only to come rapidly to the conclusion that my provisional system was no more useful or curious than, say, the classification of Swiss dragons drawn up by a Zurich naturalist in the early eighteenth century. And so I learned that the griffin originated from Hyperborea or India and the enormous roc from Arabia, that Chinese dragons possessed five, Korean four and Japanese three toes, that basilisks liked to live in damp well shafts, and that the thorny tentacles of the South American flesh-eating plant, the Ya-te-veo, caused fatal ulcers, and I agonised over whether the scarlet Mongolian death worm, olgoi-khorkhoi, belonged with the cryptids, a group in any case only loosely defined, or alternatively with the snake-like beings, yet was unable to register any noticeable advance in my understanding or gain any sense of satisfaction whatsoever.

No wonder, then, that one day I decided to invent some better monsters of my own, possibly a whole world complete with its own cosmology, a veritable Olympus, and, as so often when I find

I am getting nowhere with my writing, I turned to painting. However, the very first creature that I sketched one afternoon using a handful of watercolours I had brought with me looked more cute than terrifying, despite its scaly, bilious-green skin, the leathery webbing of its clawed feet and its runny, bloodshot eyes. Seldom have I felt so incapable, so empty and dull-headed. There was no denying that evolution was vastly more inventive than the human mind. What were the monstrous octopuses of seafaring legend compared to the giant squid's quest for a female – which was so interminable that, as he roamed the lightless ocean depths, he would unceremoniously squirt his seed under the skin of every fellow member of his species he encountered without first checking its gender? What were the crooked claws of the harpies of Greek antiquity compared to the hideous faces of the hook-nosed birds of prey of the same name, the agonising death of the nine-headed hydra decapitated by Heracles compared to the potential immortality of the freshwater Hydra polyp, or the dragon of myths and fairytales hysterically guarding its treasure compared to the sublime indifference of the giant lizards dozing on the rocks of the Galapagos Islands?

I interrupted my reading more and more frequently, stared into the embers, fingered the little nest of lichen with its sulphurous glow, painted my name in various scripts on the back of the photocopied articles on monstrosities, which I had put to one side soon after I had arrived. From time to time I would read snippets from an anthology of legends of Upper Valais I had found in a drawer of the bedside cabinet so that the wandering souls of godless servants and child murderers described therein would distract me from the monsters, I would cut my fingernails or comb my hair until the strong dark hairs lay like bookmarks in the folds of the books, look at the screen of my mobile telephone, even though there was virtually never any reception, and out of the window at the opposite side of the valley, just as if I were expecting someone or something.

Then, on the twelfth or thirteenth night, I dreamed of a bathtub full of snakes with short stout bodies which actually reminded me more of monitor lizards with their legs amputated. The strangest thing about them was that each one had a girl's head with a youthful, rosy face and blonde hair braided into long plaits. I tried speaking to them but they remained mute, and instead took off into the air and flew around the room. Their facial expressions were the only sign that they had feelings like me. When I woke up, I found myself thinking of Baku, a Japanese monster with an elephant's head, a bull's tail and the paws of a tiger which fed mostly on human nightmares, and wondered whether it would have liked the taste of mine.

I decided to take a day's break from my research and spend some time among people. The sky was overcast, and the clouds hung above the forest in loose grey plumes. The colours were pale, but for that very reason everything seemed surreally clear: the stretch of tarmacked road, the cracks in the asphalt and a bright-red mark at the edge of the road surface which might equally well have represented a serpent or a question mark gone wrong. I knew that a double-headed snake was not in itself a sign. Only the walker who encountered it turned it into one. The steeper the terrain, the shorter and quicker my steps became in an effort to compensate for the downward gradient. In the distance, a few sheep clung to the mountainside. Animals evidently coped better than humans with steep inclines and could simply live their lives on sloping ground. A temporary state that was as normal for them as level ground was for me. The slope was littered with jutting boulders looking as if they had been scattered over the landscape in deliberately random fashion, their windward side covered in moss. Hard to believe that all this had simply come about rather than having been carefully designed. Had come into being unaided and then been tamed. Although the unpredictability remained. Nature deserved credit for much more than God. All the same, I was touched by the notion that He had actually hidden the fossils of animals that had never existed in the Earth's crust just to fool us. What a lot of work for such a crude joke. For a moment I wished it were true.

As time went by I started to sweat, though it was not warm enough to be out and about in just a jumper. The hardest part was finding a rhythm for the descent, converting gravity into momentum. Behind a hill, the mist was clearing. Below me the steppe-like slopes and lower still, laid out before me and suddenly remarkably close, the light-green valley plain, the floor of what was once a sea. The realms of possibility were a fertile breeding ground, even if it was fairly unlikely that there were vertebrates thousands of years old living in labyrinthine caves inside the Earth in fear or even hope of being discovered. Might dragons in fact be faded reflections of past experiences, vestiges of ancient times? Why shouldn't memories push for their own survival, preservation and propagation in the same way that organisms do? After all, virtually nothing was more formidable, probably, than the power of images, of the once-seen. I was reminded of the incredible tales of fair-skinned women who bore black-skinned or shaggy-haired children after looking at images of St Maurice or John the Baptist at the time of conception. But if that were the way of things, what kind of creatures would populate the world? How far back could memories be traced? Beyond a certain point, everything disappeared into the fog. The ouroboros, the world serpent, bit its own tail.

The customary yellow signpost stood at the place where the paths forked. I was impressed by its presence, its minutely detailed information, its single-mindedness. Some things were indeed perfectly clear, perfectly unambiguous. My head was full of phrases and sayings. What was that lovely one again? A path is made by walking on it. Just let go. How many times had I heard that and immediately tensed up? You could think all you liked, but it didn't alter how you felt. Your whole body a fist that could only be prised open with brute force. Everything in hand, yet not that elusive heartbeat. The old you-just-have-to-believe-it. Painted slips of paper under the Christmas tree. Ultimately, the demystification of the world was the biggest fairytale of all. A child's magical thinking more powerful than any statistic, any empirical value. A counting rhyme suddenly came true, a crack in the pavement held unspeakable horrors, and anyone who stepped on it was irretrievably lost. Against myth you could only lose. True, miracles weren't out of the question, but they couldn't be taken for granted. Cause and effect were easily confused. What was desire, what was will, what merely a bodily function? Let go or hold tight? Become a vessel. Give up calculating, acknowledge something bigger than existence. Something like mercy. Something like humility. One long humiliation.

Finally, the terrain began to level out. The path now led past terraced fields and a meadow. In it stood a single cow with prominent horns, its nostrils pink and damp, a shaggy coat, not an eye to be seen, nothing but reddish-brown matted hair. The hum of electricity. A few cherry trees, the scabby bark shimmering like verdigris. And then a sense of surprise, after all, when from behind the barn I caught the glint of the grey-blue roofs of the village, a settlement perched midway between valley floor and mountain top, where the air was thin and the pasture green. The footpath joined a road. The tarmac glistened as if after rain. The place looked abandoned. There was not even a cat to be seen. The buildings were huddled so closely together that you could have jumped from roof to roof. Dwellings alternated with barns, stables and garages. In between them narrow alleys and flights of stone steps barely wider than the length of a forearm, and as dark as if they were leading straight into the bowels of the mountains, into the deeper layers of time.

From somewhere I became aware of a kind of rasping, then a dull thud, a clatter, followed by a sudden groan. It seemed to have come from the lower ground floor of a chalet. The wood of the door was old and silvery grey. A crack at knee height, just large enough to look through. I peered in. Pitch black inside. It was a while before I could make anything out. A shapeless lump in the straw, its surface slimy, a whitish, festering film streaked with blood. Whatever it was, it was still alive. Its pulse irregular, in its final throes, the beginning of the end. A growth: whether benign or malignant you only find out after the procedure. The doctor's words unequivocal: physiologically everything's tiptop. *Physiologically.* The body was always right. The lump of flesh in front of me twitched like an organ exposed in an operation. I thought of the faded, often indefinable organic matter on show in museum display cases. Preserved in formaldehyde, classified, a jumble in which the abnormal was hard to distinguish from the typical. What mattered was that it was eye-catching. The music and lighting had to be right. The rest was down to the imagination. The eye alone was stupid. The lump convulsed again, moved or was moved. A bubble appeared, full of blood. It wobbled, slid to the ground. The bundle began to wriggle, as if tied up. A battle scene. A wounded animal. All of a sudden a black mouth that descended, small pointed yellow teeth, an outstretched tongue that licked off the slime in rhythmic movements and swallowed it. A hoof that nudged the lump until it moved again, took shape, a body, individual limbs stretched out – thin, spindly black and white legs pointing crookedly upwards, a short tail, a head, the back of it flat, the face completely black. A single eye. Only now did I notice the foul smell. The odour of dirty wool, of sheep droppings, of congealed blood. I felt sick. I drew my head back. Felt a stabbing pain in my knee that only eased after a few steps. Down the deserted main street to the whitewashed church, its tall pointed spire like a screwdriver bit. The square in front with its bus stop, the post box, a red hydrant, it all looked as innocuous as a fresh crime scene in the newspaper, on the page with all the bad news, the one headed "Miscellaneous", "Panorama", or "From Around the World". Crimes that suddenly had a two-fold presence in the world – as deed and thought. One person's desire, the other's fear. Every boundary only there to be overstepped.

A little bell rang with a bright, busy sound as I entered the shop. Not a soul to be seen. The shelves were chock-full all the way up nearly to the ceiling, the colourful wares neatly arranged. A maze whose few, narrow aisles in fact only ever led to the till and back to the exit. I was not hungry or thirsty, nor did I have any desire to choose something. Perhaps I already had everything I could wish for; at any rate my basket remained empty. The bell tinkled again. A man came rushing in. He was wearing an old uniform with shiny buttons and looked at me as if he wanted me to speak to him. Passing the till, I saw a woman, the shop assistant, standing there, having seemingly appeared out of nowhere. Her gaze was as empty as if she had spent her entire life in this place, weary and simultaneously expectant. I had not noticed her before. Instinctively I grabbed a newspaper, rummaged around for some loose change. The shopkeeper called out something to the man. I did not understand a single word. And no matter how hard I tried, I would never understand any of it. She sat down, her hands dropped into her lap, and it was then that I saw it, a tattoo on the inside of her right wrist, a white horse's head with a pale blue spiral horn on its forehead, surrounded by pink clouds. My coins jangled in the little bowl. A question from the shopkeeper, a hurried shake of the head from me, and again the shame that, whenever anyone here addressed me, I could never understand a word. A cluster of gold bangles slid over the tattoo and back again. Hand and unicorn drifted up to the shopkeeper's face, she fiddled with her dyed blonde hair, patted a few strands into place. For a brief moment it was right up close, looking at me. A bright spot shone in its big blue comic-book eye. Its gaze was friendly, harmless and penetrating all at once. Then the creature was gone again, searching in the open drawer for change.

Nonetheless a sign, an unmistakable pointer. There was no ignoring it. I tried to close my eyes and ears to it, rushed out, the irritating tinkle sounded once more, then I was back in the square and turned into the main street, with rapid steps, almost light-footed, not rushing, uphill, back or away, it didn't matter. My heart suddenly loud, like on a hunt or on the run. It was easily startled, its pounding went right up into my neck. It did me good simply to walk on, to abandon myself to gravity. Step by step, away from the horn. Dragons may be vanquished, dead and buried, their fossilised bones assembled into skeletons and exhibited in museums with the aid of steel stays, but the unicorn, that vulgar, ridiculous, transparent thing, was immortal, indestructible, ubi-quitous — be it on the wrist of a cashier or in the Cabinet of Curiosities in Basel's Totengässlein. Smooth and lustrous, it had stood there, hard, the size of it breathtaking. A specimen of itself. The largest monster of all. "Do not touch," it said. As if I might have been wanting to stroke the ivory, calcium phosphate turned on nature's lathe. An antidote to any poison. A miracle remedy. But I was not ill. I was tiptop. And not so desperate that I would fall for a horn. After all, I was no longer a virgin. Although in its eyes perhaps I was. What would it do with me, then, in the middle of the forest? Nestle its head against my breast or lay its horn in my lap? Really it all amounted to the same thing. The joys of virginity? Where there's a horn there's a hole. The hymen, too, was merely an enemy to be speared. An apple needing picking. If only it were that simple.

The road curved around, and beyond it, on a plateau, a small village appeared, its blackish-brown houses huddled around the church, surrounded by grazing land, perched above a steep rocky drop, barely a hundred metres away but separated from me by a ravine. Not far from the precipice, two brown horses were grazing in a paddock. They stood facing in opposite directions, with not their heads but their tails turned towards each other, mirror images, as if wearing an invisible harness and awaiting their orders. That scene looked familiar. But from where? Two horses, rear to rear. From school, an illustration in a history book, a drawing in shades of sepia. A picture showing horses straining in opposite directions, their necks thrusting forward beneath the whip, the huge effort, their bits covered in foam. Lines of sweat under their harnesses. Two six-horse or even eight-horse teams, their heads turned away. And between them an orb with everything sucked out of it: a vacuum, an unimaginable void, a dead space. Behind it the panorama of a hilly landscape, and above it, floating in the sky, two hemispheres, a pair of divine, blind eyeballs. Nothing was more terrible than empty space. And every single monster there solely to fill it, to obscure the blind spot of fear, making it doubly invisible. A feeling in my stomach, lifeless and heavy. No boulder in sight, nowhere to sit down. I stopped walking, dropped into a squat. My insides a clenched fist. Is this what emptiness felt like? How heavy was emptiness? The realms of possibility were a fertile breeding ground. The realms of impossibility too. A white delivery van thundered past me. I crossed the road, discovered on the other side a dark opening in the undergrowth, a sunken path, a channel that dug itself ever deeper into the forest, the brushwood like a wall on each side.

Bare deciduous trees, then before long the shade of fir trees. The ground was spongy and strewn with copper-coloured needles. A hollow knocking was audible from somewhere. Otherwise it was completely quiet. My footsteps deadened, almost soundless. The path meandering aimlessly. It descended along a gorge for a time, then carried on close to the rock face, until eventually it fizzled out altogether on a shady knoll. The terrain now became more open, affording a view of the broad western basin. The mountain flanks protruded into the lowlands like pieces of stage scenery. Glinting in the haze was the river from which the valley took its name. Now I also saw, not that far off, a bare patch in the forest where the trees were lying higgledy-piggledy like fallen matches. Alpine choughs screeched high above, let themselves fall and then climbed their way back up beyond the tree line. Behind them, a semi-derelict barn clung to the slope, unreachable, like a paint-ing – framed by the white of the snow, as remote as summer. Incredible that there could actually be a track leading to it. Where were the signposts when you needed them? On an embankment, a handful of stones between two lumps of rock, piled in layers, almost a flight of steps, a pointer, the hint of a path. Pains in my knees, in my groin, in my lower back. Why couldn't my body just work the way it said in the textbook? What had I done to it that it was reluctant to obey? That it did whatever it wanted. And not what I wanted. The path was getting ever steeper now, more like a chamois track. It was better on all fours anyway. At least that way I made some headway. I felt my way up, crawled through loose shale and scree until there was more vegetation again, a sparse covering of grass, almost a meadow. Then a house, then another, a whole group scattered over a mountainside. A settle-ment, a little village. And then the white chapel, the water trough. It was the hamlet, my hamlet! The same place I had set out from hours ago. As if I had known the answer to a riddle all along. All my ramblings for nothing. I couldn't even get lost properly. Was I relieved, or was I disappointed? Probably both. A thin plume of smoke rose from one of the chimneys, and there was a red car in the small car park. I was no longer alone.

The living room was cold, the stove giving out no warmth. The logs simply wouldn't light. In the end, I helped things along with a stack of photocopies, until the flames finally sent some sparks flying. Even after supper there was no let-up in the pain. It felt as if something was drilling into my innards. My legs leaden. Then, on the loo during the night, the blackish-brown blood in my pants. A sign, as unmistakable as the dull ache in my lower abdomen and the pain in my breasts. The newspaper lay on the tiles, on its front page the photograph of a forest after a fire, a hazy landscape with charred tree trunks and spindly green pine trees. By the time I finally fell asleep, it was already getting light outside. A few hours later I woke up. Everything was bathed in a grey haze, which initially I took for fog until I realised that it was clouds that had drifted down from higher altitudes. I put wood on the fire, went back to bed and browsed a guide to Alpine wildlife until my eyes went woozy and I nodded off. When I awoke again, the clouds had grown denser. It was so silent that the thought briefly crossed my mind that mankind had perished. The thought did not frighten me; on the contrary, it was comforting. I cleared the books off the table, washed my laundry in the sink, hung it up over the stove and cooked myself a few shrivelled potatoes. In the evening I opened a bottle of red wine I had found under the sink. Then I decided to paint a self-portrait, but the only mirror was on the wall of the unheated bathroom and I couldn't manage to release it from its brackets.

A few days later, as I was heading home from a walk, a man came towards me. He was small and his skin smooth as leather. Apparently pleased to see me, he immediately started chattering

away to me in animated fashion, and unusually fast for that
dialect. It seemed to be about something important. I told him
that I couldn't understand what he was saying. He repeated his
litany, just as rapidly as before, until I shook my head again. He
had blackish-brown, deep-set eyes protected by bushy brows.
He looked at me, then at my boots and walked on without any
gesture of regret or apology.

That night there was a thunderstorm with persistent sheet
lightning. The storm tore at the shutters. As I was unable to sleep,
I took a look at the photographs in the wildlife guide, and spotted among them the neon-green weave that was now gracing my
kitchen table. It was the wolf lichen, which is highly toxic to the
nervous systems of carnivorous vertebrates. I took the dry, green
bundle and a shovel and buried it behind the house in the rain.
Then I spent a long time washing my hands, arms and face with
washing-up liquid. Finally, I fell into a deep, exhausted sleep.

When I woke up in the morning, a cuckoo was calling. I heeded
its call and went out. A warm fall wind was blowing. The jagged
outline of the mountain ridge against the pale-blue sky looked
like a paper cutout. It was hard to tell whether the sky had pushed
in front of the mountains, or the mountains in front of the
clouds. Dew lay on the grass. The white patches in the forest
had melted to dots. The rushing sound was audible even from a
distance. The ravine now had water flowing through it which
plunged, gurgling, into the depths. The thaw had begun. I went
back, packed my things, vacuumed, hid the key behind the firewood stacked against the wall and set off downhill towards the
valley.

Valle Inferno
VILLA SACCHETTI
also known as *Villa al Pigneto del Marchese Sacchetti*

* *Commissioned by brothers Giulio and Marcello Sacchetti and built between 1628 and 1648, Villa Sacchetti is regarded as the most important early work of master builder Pietro da Cortona.*
† *Towards the end of the seventeenth century the mansion is already starting to deteriorate. In the mid eighteenth century both wings of the building collapse. The last remnants of the ruins are taken away after 1861.*

Like every ruler, this city has two bodies. Its mortal one lies there like a defiled corpse; a quarry whose marble burns to lime in the furnaces. The pale stone harbours no fossils, yet is itself an imprint of a prehistoric age, a raw block of memory. But its immortal body rises out of the spoil heap in the imagination of strangers daydreaming before the ruins, who pause, frozen in awe, as a whole army of noble and distinguished sons, led by painters, copper engravers and literary figures, marches into the city and besieges the inns around the Spanish Square. Year in, year out, artists from northern latitudes step down from dusty stage-coaches, a letter of recommendation from some house of high standing, an allowance from a patron or an academy grant in their leather bag – and undoubtedly the address of some fellow countryman who came here many years ago for one winter and has stayed ever since.

They revere the ruins like relics, hoping for their resurrection, insatiably enraptured by lost splendour. Something is always missing. The eye sees, the mind completes: fragments become buildings, the deeds of the dead spring to life, more glorious and perfect than ever. It was here, in the Holy City, the capital of history, that the preservation of monuments was first invented and an entire people proclaimed as heirs, when the Roman Senate decided to protect the more than thousand-year-old Doric column erected in honour of Trajan and his victories, in order that it might remain whole and unscathed for as long as the world exists, and to impose the highest punishment on anyone who so much as attempted to cause it harm. Rome has not fallen; the past is not over; it is just that the future has already begun. This place is stuck between ages, between all the architectural styles vying, in this global arena, for the favour of the public who have always flocked here: Romanesque basilicas with triumphal arches sunk in sand, mediaeval gables with the façades of Baroque churches, pale Renaissance villas with sooty pyramids — an enormous, tangled organism composed of dead and living matter, governed by chance and necessity and the law of the sun.

No barrier separates the ruins from the miserable working lives of their occupants, who do not stand in awe, but live as they would anywhere else: half-naked beggars loitering in arcades; fishmongers hawking their perishable wares in the shade of a bricked-up portico; women washing their linen in ancient thermal baths; shepherds cramming their sheep into dank temples, where the one-time sacrificial animals graze at the foot of pagan altars; day labourers salvaging blocks of porous, yellowish-white travertine from the catacombs of the Flavian Amphitheatre, where the bones of wild animals and unshakeable Christians lie. Anything serviceable is used for construction or shipped. Trade in spolia is flourishing. The ruins are pure capital: not treasures to be recovered, but semi-precious minerals to be extracted, just like copper from the Alban Hills.

Few are concerned about the preservation of the Roman ruins, certainly no-one as passionate and combative as Giovanni Battista Piranesi, originally of Venice, who falls out with anyone who offers him encouragement or affection. So it almost verges on the miraculous that this man, who prefers the company of stones to that of human beings, in his thirty-third year finds a wife who tolerates him and bears him five children, even though he invests the whole of her not inconsiderable dowry in a massive hoard of copper plates. Besides his tendency to be quarrelsome and irascible, the tall man with the smouldering dark eyes is also given to single-minded devotion and self-sacrifice, and the person who claimed that even a quarter of an hour in his company would make you ill has missed what it is that truly ails the choleric type with the clouded brow: the ruins speak to him as if in a fever, rob him of his peace and sleep, constantly evoke images, visions, which he thinks he has to capture in order to prove wrong any future generations and ignoramuses who dare to claim that ancient Greek art was superior to Roman. Besotted like a man in love, he blames the vacuousness of the present, whose pitiful naivety, as he declares in pamphlet after pamphlet, is enough to drive anyone familiar with the immense grandeur of the past to despair. And Piranesi is familiar with it, has beheld it, for the ancients have populated his dreams ever since, as a child, he read about it in the annals of a Roman historian, in the living room – bathed as it was in the shimmering light of the lagoon – of his uncle, an engineer, whose job it was to maintain the defences designed to keep the intrusive Adriatic Sea at bay.

And since the present, coral-like, always colonises that which is sinking, his not old but already ponderous body is magnetically drawn into the depths, into the bowels of the Earth, into the underground vaults and catacombs, out to the sunken burial sites by the main thoroughfares beyond the city gates, whence the

ancient Romans had banished their dead, since there was nothing
on Earth they feared more than Pluto's underworld. There they
had erected necropolises for them, which now held only the
ashes of the deceased, ever since countless wars had taught them
that cremation alone prevents the corpses from being defiled by
the enemy.

So Piranesi hacks his way, with axe and flaming torch, through
the undergrowth and darkness, lights fires to ward off snakes
and scorpions, wrapped in a black cloak, bathed in moonlight like
a figure from some nineteenth-century novel. With pickaxe and
spade he digs his way into the earth, uncovers plinths and sarcophagi, measures the fortifications of old defensive structures
and the buttresses and piers of weather-beaten bridges, examines
masonry bonds and the order of columns, studies façades and
foundations, deciphers the inscriptions on ancient sepulchres,
copies the fluting on columns and the mouldings on arches,
sketches the ground plans and elevations of buried predator cages
and theatre arenas, the cross-sections and longitudinal sections
of forts and theological colleges choked with vegetation – and
draws with a restless hand the levers and beams, the hooks and
chains, the pivots and brackets that were needed to construct
those formidable structures. For him no stone is so mute, no
masonry so brittle, no truncated column so damaged that he
would not recognise in them the limbs and muscles that once
formed the strapping body of this city, and the blood vessels and
organs that once supplied it: bridges and arterial roads, aque-
ducts and water reservoirs, and in particular the many-branching
channels of the labyrinthine *Cloaca Maxima*, which, although or
indeed because it served the basest of needs, he names as the pinnacle of all architecture, whose glory, in his judgment, surpasses
even the Seven Wonders of the World. And just as the anatomist
Vesalius a century earlier dismembered the still warm corpses of

condemned murderers on the dissecting table, so he does with the dilapidated buildings, remnants of a past empire which, to his mind, was not to blame for its demise.

From the eloquent ruins, the architect, who his whole life long will never build a single house, sketches the ground plan of an imagined past and simultaneously the vision of an entirely new creation which, in his copperplate etchings, captivates more people than any building anchored to solid ground. His gaze effortlessly penetrates sediment and other material as, in his workshop, he bends over the cold, smooth-polished metal and copies the impermanent red chalk sketches onto the etching ground, an infinite number of dashes, dots and flicks, patchy shapes and vibrating lines that seldom intersect, even though they change direction with every detail as if setting out on a new course. He immerses the plate in the bath and, with each repetition, covers some areas and gives others a drizzling, so that the acid still eats into the slightest hollow and captures for ever what he does not want to forget, what he cannot forget.

When the rollers release the large sheets, the sun shines mercilessly on the etchings, the shading is velvety and black as oblivion, the architectural sightlines almost endless, the visual angles fantastical and the crumbling buildings colossal even from a bird's-eye view. The monuments stand up boldly against an inflamed sky, below them an army of tiny figures, gawky Harlequins with flailing arms. This city must have been built by giants, Roman Cyclopses at the zenith of their creative powers.

Piranesi's etchings are soon all the rage as anatomical records of ancient life, even though most of the plates tell only of death. They show interior views of burial chambers, ground plans of mausoleums, sarcophagi enthroned on marble plinths, or a cross-section through the cobblestones of a gateway leading to a crematorium. Piranesi becomes the high priest of a death cult that grips the entire continent and every week spurs new disciples to make a pilgrimage to the master's house on the far side of Monte Cavallo, to which the latter has retreated to find some peace in which to work, which was sorely lacking at his old workshop on the magnificent Corso, where he was plagued by hordes of visitors. When the beardless folk ask to be admitted, he calls out "Piranesi is not at home" until they give up without having caught a glimpse of their idol.

Only once, on one particularly hot and humid afternoon in early summer, the knocking simply does not cease. When Piranesi throws open the door with the usual cursing, on the threshold stands an elegantly dressed young man with shoulder-length, curly hair carefully combed and held together in a ribbon at the nape of his neck, smooth facial features and small round eyes that sparkle, and from his well-formed mouth, accompanied by an old-fashioned sweeping bow, come the words, spoken with a fine French accent, that he has been murmuring to himself for days, trying to strike the right tone: "Sir, if I may. My name is Hubert Robert. I love the ruins as you do. Take me with you anywhere you please."

Two years later, on the morning of a misty autumn day in the year 1760, Hubert Robert walks out of the Porta Angelica, follows the winding course of a small, partially dried-up stream into a valley at the shady far end of which, he was told, there stands a crumbling mansion. Beneath the cloud-covered sky the colours appear washed out. He breathes in the damp air, wants to shake off his tiredness, a leaden weariness which has been bothering him for some time, and which is fundamentally alien to his being.

He is young, twenty-seven years of age, a scholar of the Académie de France, the son of a Parisian valet in the service of a diplomat at the court of Versailles. He arrived in Rome, via Basel,

St Gotthard and Milan, six years ago as a member of the entourage of the diplomat's son, in order, as one gifted man among many, to draw all the monuments and buildings that, rather than concealing the signs of the times, display them almost proudly. Only this spring he travelled to Naples and visited the new excavations on the Gulf, saw Pozzuoli and Paestum, and in Tivoli drew the gnarled olive trees reaching with their parched branches towards a copper-coloured sky in the derelict interior of a Temple of the Sibyl. He had not wanted to spend another summer in the feverish heat of Rome, which a year earlier had almost cost him his life. Since his return, he is somehow changed. Beset by a strange weariness that has suddenly spoiled his enjoyment of all the ancient remains, he is seized by an urge to visit some ruins from his own era, namely those of the villa of the Sacchettis, which, after another bend in the path, now appears behind the branches of the cypresses at the end of a sandy avenue.

He leaves the bridle path behind, makes his way towards the grounds, sits down on the hard, brown grass and looks. Then he starts drawing the tumbledown premises, quickly and accurately, just as, during the long evenings of his first Roman winter, he drew the muscles of a wiry Italian in the high-ceilinged painting room of the academy on the Corso. He guides his graphite pencil purposefully over the paper, rarely looks up, capturing the scene with only an occasional glance: the way the straggly garden extends up over the slope in three tiers, the way the crumbling building, a pavilion with a protruding façade and two curved wings, sits enthroned on an embankment as if on a pedestal, at its centre the tall semicircular apse, a water feature on each of the three terraces: a fountain, a fishpond and a shady nymphaeum with Doric pilasters behind a colonnade. But the flights of steps are bare except for the crumbling stonework. The roof structure is disintegrating, the balustrades are falling down, the coffered half-dome of the apse is cracked, the fountain without water, and the seashell-shaped basin guarded by a pair of Tritons is bone-dry right down to its stone floor. Even the lintel above the entrance has slipped lower as if after an earthquake.

Robert draws all of this, allowing himself to add the familiar figures of the household staff to the abandoned scene: on the sheet of paper a girl balances a jug on her head, a woman holds an infant to her breast, another leads a child up the steps, a dog follows an invisible scent, a cow and a sheep stand by the fountain, and a donkey lowers his head to the basin, which is filled to the brim with water.

Hubert Robert casts an eye over his drawing, rolls up the sheet of paper, crosses the overgrown track that was once the drive, ascends the cracked steps, past the mortar remnants scattered at the foot of the wall. The entrance is littered with rubble. He climbs inside through a window aperture, a cool room of not particularly large dimensions, which must once have been the drawing room. A musty odour hangs in the air. Broken roof tiles and rotten beams lie in a heap on the ground; barely an arch of the vault is intact. And in the middle of the coffered ceiling is a gaping hole like a giant wound with the whitish-grey bank of clouds shining through. Only around the edges, under the crumbling plaster, is it still possible to make out the remains, rimmed black with mould, of a ceiling painting, faded scenes populated with shadowy figures, the only distinguishable one depicting an impaled head with wide-staring eyes – a grisly vision that reminds Robert of a line from Virgil's *Aeneid*: "*Unum pro multis dabitur caput.*" One head will be sacrificed for many.

He stares at the gruesome head until a thought strikes him: the present is merely the past of the future. – A shudder comes over him, he clambers over the rubble and steps back, strangely elated, into the open, but then a foul smell hits him, bringing back memories of the previous summer, of the intolerable stench which, in August, after the heavy rains, when the Tiber was swollen and as so often had burst its banks, had settled like a belljar over the entire city and dissipated only briefly during the twilight hours when he, like everyone else, took the opportunity to go for a stroll to recuperate from the heat of the day. Later he was told by the doctor, a thoughtful and experienced man who trusted above all in the salutary effect of bloodletting, that during those eerily fresh evening hours he must have been infected with the swamp fever, which few survive. Nobody – neither his landlady nor his friends – had still believed Robert would recover, so far advanced was his physical deterioration and accompanying mental breakdown. After the tenth bloodletting in the space of eight days, he too, coming round after fainting from lack of blood, was himself so resigned to his own irrevocable end that, even as the symptoms were already receding, he was still expecting to die and is surprised to this day to have survived the illness.

He turns around once more, surveys the house, which now seems to him transformed. Greenery sprouts from the walls, moss covers the marble gods, stonecrop springs from the cracks, ivy clings to the stone with its sturdy roots, Virginia creeper adorns the parapet, its many-branching tendrils twining themselves around the fragile cartouche which identifies the builder and still bears the royal coat of arms of the Sacchetti family, three black stripes on a white background.

When Giulio Sacchetti was appointed a cardinal over one hundred years ago, he had commissioned this villa with its high apse, proud and imposing like that of the Belvedere – a summer house in Valle Inferno, a sandy depression between Monte Mario and the Vatican, a dusty wooded hollow near the papal state, full of tall pines and slender cypresses. He is a rich man, Rome's wealthiest cardinal – with a glittering future in prospect. From the bedrooms of his summer residence he can see the dome of St Peter's Basilica. Twice he hopes to be elected Pontifex Maximus, and at the conclave in 1655 he is not far short. But others become pope.

One year later he stands at the window of his country house for the last time and gazes again at the object of his failed dreams, in his bony hand a perfumed sachet containing herbs, bitter orange and lemon peel, which he keeps pressing to his nose. The plague is raging in the city – yet again, but with more devastating effect than in a long time. The streets are populated with figures enveloped in clouds of smoke, wearing beaked masks in an attempt to ward off the disease with aromatic vapours of myrrh, camphor and wild calla – and carrying a stick to keep the sick at bay, those poor devils who are carried off so quickly that he, Giulio Sacchetti, papal adviser on disease control, can come up with nothing better than having the wretched dead buried outside the city walls – as swiftly as possible and without any manner of religious ritual – before decomposition can set in and the corpses emit their reputedly highly infectious effluvia. This secluded valley is particularly prone to miasmas, those damp mists that fester in the shallow margins and spongy banks of bodies of still water, hang low above the earth – and exude a stench so repulsive that it is inevitably perceived as toxic and sinister. Giulio Sacchetti knows what is written in every treatise on the plague: a piece of land, once contaminated, is lost for ever. From now on he receives his guests in his city palazzo again. Only a few decades after its construction, Villa Sacchetti is abandoned.

First the tiled roof sags, then the rotten beams warp under the colossal weight of the vault. Soon water trickles through the cracked tiles, seeps into the timbers and walls, and the disintegration begins. The house's outlines, which a young master builder once traced on the drawing board with a ruler, are gradually losing their shape, crumbling and unravelling. The stone, once cut and layered to make walls, becomes weak and vulnerable, defence-less in the face of weeds and weather, to the point that there is no distinguishing what is tuff, what is slate, what is marble and what is rock. Only the thick, sturdy outer walls of the pavilion will stand firm for a while longer against the water that, in the summer months, cascades down the hillside after every down-pour as if the end of the world were nigh.

Meanwhile in Paris, Europe's other capital, the stench of bodily excretions reigns longer than the House of Bourbon – a vile odour of urine and faeces. At night, especially, it engulfs whole districts, when the sewer emptiers climb back out of the cesspits and, to spare themselves the trip to the waste dump, tip the excre-ment into the gutter, a viscous sauce which, as dawn breaks, runs down the streets towards the Seine, on the banks of which the water carriers later fill their jugs, oblivious.

Early infirmity will deliver them. There is a bed ready for each one of them in the Hôtel-Dieu, the ancient hospital in the laby-rinthine old town, a bed they must share with four others. There the insane and the elderly lie alongside orphans, women who have just given birth and post-operative patients one floor up from the corpses, the sick among the dying. The walls are damp, the corridors poorly ventilated, and even on summer days, a perpetual twilight filters through the window openings. The chil-dren smell sour, the women sickly sweet, the men of cold sweat, and hanging over everything is the foetid odour of decay which – as surely as the incessant fumbling with the bedclothes – heralds the approach of death, as on the night of December 30 of the year 1772, when a fire accidentally started during candle-dipping jumps across to the timberwork and spreads to the entire warren-like compound. For two weeks of winter the hospital is in flames. As the inferno takes hold, destroying an ever-expanding tract of the old heart of the city, spectators revel in the spectacle that is bathing the cityscape in a red glow.

What is left is a hollowed-out shell against a black sky, which Hubert Robert captures in several drawings and paintings. He has been back in Paris for eight years, and has earned himself the nickname "Robert des Ruines". Ruins are in demand. Anyone who cannot wait for time to do its work has them built or painted. The collapse of a building attracts almost as many onlookers as an execution. So Robert paints monks preaching in ancient temples and washerwomen on the quaysides of underground rivers, the demolition of houses on the Pont Notre-Dame and Pont au Change; he paints the horse carts taking the rubble from the ruins and men loading whatever is left behind onto barges, the day labourers hunting for reusable materials on the battlefields of urban regeneration and piling them up for sale, to keep the eternal cycle in motion. And so ruins turn into building sites, the one indistinguishable from the other in Robert's paintings. On his canvas even the ditch for the foundations of the school of surgery resembles an archaeological excavation. He paints the blaze at the opera house as an erupting volcano, the sea of flames, the pillar of fire and the clouds of smoke against a June night sky, the sooty pall of the morning after, as well as the levelling of the Château of Meudon, the demolition of the Church of the Feuillants and the storming of the Bastille, the black bulwark before it was razed to the ground – a compelling, eloquent image: the falling lumps of stone pile up in the moat like ancient spolia, clouds of smoke billowing all around them. The new, says this picture, demands the ruthless destruction of the old. From now on, monuments disappear every day; every week a cavalcade of statues is dispatched to the furnace. Paris is the new city of ruins. Palaces are stormed, fortresses torn down, churches laid waste, and skeletons of kings and queens, abbots and cardinals, princes of the noblest blood dragged from their graves, their lead and copper coffins melted down to make shotgun pellets in purpose-built foundries and the bones consigned to hastily dug pits and sprinkled with the kind of unslaked lime that suppresses the stench of corpses and hastens their decomposition. Robert paints his panorama of purposeful and purposeless destruction with the stoical equanimity of a chronicler. Anyone at the time who asks him which side he is on receives the answer: "On the side of art."

In his picture, the desecration of the centuries-old tombs becomes an everyday exercise and it is impossible to tell whether something is being destroyed or preserved here. Before the canvas is even dry, he is arrested. Like so many other protégés of the aristocracy, he ends up in Saint-Lazare, the prison that was once a leper colony. There, too, he paints: the distribution of milk, the ball games in the prison yard, the suburbs of Clichy and La Chapelle glinting in the distance through the barred window, and the fields lying fallow around Montmartre, which rises up on the horizon – on earthenware and door timbers at first, until he is given permission to acquire canvases and paper. Every afternoon he practises gymnastics in the inner yard, not far from an enormous wooden cross, at the foot of which a marquise cloaked in black begs heaven for mercy – and the restoration of the old order, when "a lord was still a lord, and a servant still a servant".

One March evening in 1794 laughter issues from the third-floor corridor. Not unusually, there is a feast in progress, pike and trout are served, fruit and wine. A little monkey roams from cell to cell and Émile, the five-year-old son of a prisoner, takes a rabbit for a walk on a lead, to general amusement. Two female inmates play the harpsichord and harp, oblivious of everyone around them, then once the instruments have fallen silent, Robert starts telling the story of how, as a young man, he had scaled the Colosseum and almost fallen, and how he had plucked up the courage to call on Piranesi. How he was mentored by him and allowed to draw the subterranean burial sites with him. He makes no mention of the gruesome picture in Villa Sacchetti. As always he wears a knee-length purple robe, beneath which his bodily proportions can only be guessed at. He has two deep wrinkles etched into his high forehead, and a few pockmarks dotting his otherwise rosy, smooth face. His black, bushy eyebrows are now as grey as his sparse hair. In spite of his age and his corpulence, he nearly always wins the games of catch in the prison yard. And his small eyes are as cheerful as ever. When he laughs, his fleshy lower lip trembles, and two dimples appear on his chin. He raises his wine glass and proclaims contentedly that he is the least unhappy inmate in Saint-Lazare. He does not, though, speak of the reason for his unshakeable gaiety: that absolute certainty that he, like everyone here, will die by the guillotine. – "*Stat sua cuique dies*," he says, quoting Virgil, as he so often does, and laughs his infectious laugh that would have you believe that misfortune had never befallen him. Yet his four children are all dead, borne away by illness. He is fully prepared. He has already done a painting of his own grave and built himself a miniature guillotine out of scraps of firewood to familiarise himself with the workings of the apparatus that before long, when his turn comes, will nice and neatly sever his head from his body. Every few days, the drum roll announcing the arrival of the dark horsecarts that come to fetch the prisoners and take them before the court echoes through his cell.

A few weeks later, on a cold, clear sunny morning in May 1794, he is standing among the prisoners gathered in the inner yard when his name is called out. He realises that his final hour has come and is about to step forward when another man makes himself known, someone on whom fate has bestowed the same surname, who will now face the blade in his place. Hubert Robert is released. Only many years later does he eventually die of a stroke in his studio in rue Neuve de Luxembourg. He drops dead on the floor, his palette in his hand.

One year after Robert's death, in July 1809, two architects accompanied by a doctor take a drive into the deserted, muggy valley near Rome. Since the horses start to take fright before they have reached their destination, and even the whip cannot persuade them to pull the carriage all the way to the end of the almost impassable avenue, the men have no choice but to finish their journey on foot, until they are standing in front of Villa Sacchetti with Monte Mario behind it, the hill on which all Rome's occupiers set up camp, including Napoleon's staff officer in February 1797, when he issued the order to seize all works of art deemed worthy of being transported back to the French Republic, the self-proclaimed land of freedom, to Paris, school for all the world, whereupon the officers fanned out across the city and plundered the pope's treasure chambers, cut up Raphael's tapestries, sawed frescos and paintings to pieces, hacked the limbs off statues.

While their fathers had come here to marvel, they came to steal what they had marvelled at. All the metal, all the marble in the churches was prised free and sold, the tombs of the saints ransacked, gold reliquaries, monstrances and tabernacles auctioned off, high altars smashed that even the Goths had spared, and all the insignia of the nobility wiped from the face of the city: the oak tree of the della Rovere family, the bull of the Borgias, the balls of the Medicis, the lilies of the Farneses, the bees of the Barberinis and the three black stripes of the Sacchettis, which survived the frenzy only out here in the Valle Inferno.

The gentlemen ascend the dilapidated steps. They are looking for a place for the dead, a cemetery for all. The two architects want to turn the ruins into a chapel and the grounds into an airy, expansive necropolis shaded by high walls, because all the burial grounds inside the Aurelian Walls were closed soon after the pope was taken prisoner and carted off to France like some particularly precious find. Rome's treasures have gone, Apollo, Laocoön, even the Belvedere Torso, paraded as trophies on ox-drawn chariots decked out with laurel, from the Jardin des Plantes, past the Panthéon to the Champ-de-Mars, together with African camels, lions and a bear from Bern, a two-day-long triumphal procession under a leaden sky, which cleared towards the evening of the first day, prompting self-important reporters to comment that the sun had prevailed over the clouds as had the forces of freedom over those of tyranny.

Only the weighty Trajan's Column still stands where it has always stood. Rome has lost nearly a third of its population; it now has more dwellings than residents. Palaces and monasteries are crumbling ruins, and from the crypts of churches comes the familiar, sickly sweet smell of decay, even though doctors warn in notices and lectures of the dangers emanating from the decomposing corpses, and urgently recommend that the dead be buried outside the city gates. From now on, the law of hygiene must apply, superseding traditional ritual. Yet the Romans refuse, do not want to bury their dead out in the bare soil of the Valle Inferno, but to inter them in boxes of stone, in mausoleums and crypts, near the bones of the saints, as they always have done.

The cemetery is never inaugurated. Brambles grow in the Colosseum. There is digging in the Forum. Sand begins to submerge the villa in its valley; sheep graze on the avenue. Pines and cypresses exude their delicately aromatic scent, and for a long time painters keep coming, until the very last of the surviving remains have sunk into the ground as well.

Manhattan
THE BOY IN BLUE
or *Emerald of Death*

* *Friedrich Wilhelm Murnau's first film was shot in spring 1919 at the moated castle of Vischering in the Münster region, and in the countryside around Berlin. The plot revolved around a painting based on Thomas Gainsborough's "The Blue Boy", with the face replaced by that of Murnau's protagonist Thomas van Weerth, played by silent movie star Ernst Hofmann. There are various accounts of the film's plot, but in all of them the principal character, the last of the family line, is living an impoverished, lonely life in the castle of his fore-fathers with only an old servant for company. He often contemplates the por-trait of one of his ancestors, with whom he feels a mysterious affinity, not merely because of their strong physical resemblance. Is he the reincarnation of this young man in blue, who wears on his breast the notorious Emerald of Death, which has only ever brought bad luck to his family? To keep the curse at bay, one of his ancestors has hidden the emerald. One night Thomas has a dream in which the "Boy in Blue" climbs out of the painting and leads him to the hiding place. When Thomas wakes up, he does in fact find the emerald in the place indicated, and ignores his old servant's pleas to throw the jewel away. Meanwhile a band of minstrels turns up at the castle. They steal the emerald, burn down the castle and destroy the portrait, leaving him with nothing. Thomas falls ill, but survives thanks to the true love and selfless devotion of a pretty actress.*

† *No record of the premiere of the silent movie has been found to date. It was probably never screened as a main feature, for it is not mentioned by any of the contemporary critics. It is considered lost. The Deutsche Kinemathek in Berlin holds in its nitrate film collection thirty-five short fragments of the film in five different tints.*

She must've caught a cold. Her nose was running. Had she even been blocked up? Not that she could remember. Which made her suspicious. After all, she did her best to look after her health. Where were those damn Kleenex? The pack was right here a moment ago. What a nuisance. There was no way she was going anywhere without tissues. Ah, there they were, under the mirror! Right, in the purse they go, hat on, sunglasses on, close the door and let's roll. What the hell was that strange whiff in the hall? Ah, that's it. It was soft-soap Monday. Every week the cleaning crew from Queens would turn up at some unearthly hour and scrub the marble like a gang of crazed monkeys, and she found herself rudely awakened at the crack of dawn. No-one else in the entire building got up as early as she did. The stink left by the char-women was bound to hang around until Wednesday at least. She would have to think about moving yet again. Was there no end to it? It was enough to make you weep. Luckily the elevator arrived quickly. The boy could've been a bit more polite, though. Had no-one told him who he was dealing with? Pretending not to recognize her. Hadn't anyone told him how to greet her? Barely out of diapers and already gone to the dogs. Probably getting ideas in his head. After all, there was no-one else in the elevator. That's all she needed. It seemed to be taking for ever. But then it *was* seventeen floors. Finally they made it. At least the doorman did things the proper way, came out of his lodge and opened the door for her. You're welcome. Heaven! The coast was clear. No vultures in sight. No-one noticed her. Probably because of the new sunglasses. O.K. then. She wasn't choosy, so she just went for the first guy to come along, a man in a gray flannel suit. He wasn't that elegant, to be honest. But a good choice all the same. He walked fast towards the East Side, piloted her through the crush, gave her a direction, a rhythm. That in itself was a good thing. Sometimes he disappeared in the crowd, but she soon caught up with him again. After all, she was a seasoned pedestrian. It was the only field she'd become remotely expert in. Basically it was her only pleasure, her religion. If need be she could get by without her calisthenics, but definitely not without her walks. Her outings to browse the store windows, her wanderings, her random detours. At least one hour a day, preferably two. Usually down to Washington Square Park and back, sometimes up to 77th Street. It was good to follow close on someone's heels to start with. She'd have an aimless wander later. After all you couldn't get lost. One advantage of islands.

It was colder than she thought. Too cold for April at any rate. Even by East Coast standards. It was always either freezing cold or boiling hot in this city. God knows why she even lived here, in this unpardonable, drafty climate where you catch a cold at the drop of a hat. She should've gone to California back in March. Just as she normally did. March would've been right, March rather than later. O.K., it was deadly boring there when you had nothing to do. But all the same, the climate was perfect: fresh air, plenty of sunshine. You could run around butt-naked all day. Well in theory anyway. Too bad Schleesky hated it. It meant she had to sort everything out herself: a flight, a driver and even someplace to stay now that the house was sold and Mabery Road was no longer an option either. As if she didn't already have enough on her plate. For weeks she'd been hunting for the right sweater. It had to be cashmere. In dusty pink, her favorite color. She loved colors: salmon, mauve, hot pink. But none as much as dusty pink. She also had appointments, stupid meetings. She canceled most of them, but it was tiring all the same. Cecil had been at it again. He obviously imagined he could simply suggest any time, any place or, worse still, ask her to suggest something. How was she supposed to know whether she would be hungry or thirsty or wanting to see him tomorrow or in three days' time?

Not to mention her poorly state. Her health had never been the best. Even though she took good care of herself, always dressed warmly enough and never, ever sat down on the toilet seat. That was just how it was: a puff of wind and she was laid low with some damn wretched cold. The last time was when she had tea with Mercedes. She'd only leaned against the open window briefly. But by that evening her throat was sore as hell, and even though she'd gone to bed wearing two sweaters and woolen tights as always, she'd woken up the next morning feeling at death's door. It was weeks before she was anywhere near back on form. In fact, it was simpler to say when she *hadn't* been ill. And on top of that the goddamn hot flushes out of the blue. What a pain in the ass. She urgently needed new panties. She'd even seen those light-blue knee-length ones in London last fall. Cecil had said in his letter that Lillywhites only stocked them in royal blue, bright scarlet and canary yellow. He should've looked in Harrods then. After all, he had promised to track some down for her. To think she was having to deal with that now as well. Perhaps she ought to meet with him after all, if only on account of the panties.

Hey, what had gotten into the gray suit? He'd just veered off-course, drifted over to the right and approached the bank of windows. What the heck! Surely he wasn't going to . . . or maybe he was. No! No way! He made a beeline for it. And disappeared through the revolving doors of the Plaza, of all places! Just as she'd gotten used to him. It could at least have been the Waldorf Astoria! Wild horses couldn't drag her into the Plaza. It had the scruffiest rear entrance in the city. That such a swanky hotel could have such a foul-smelling backyard. She knew a bit about rear entrances. Yes, if only she knew as much about everything else as she did about rear entrances! About garbage cans and those hampers full of stinking dirty linen and the service elevators reeking of leftover food. Just her luck! Not even ten o'clock and already she'd had her first disappointment, not counting the elevator boy. She should just stop having anything to do with other people.

Now there she stood with a runny nose, snot trickling down. And no-one to stop it. What a nightmare! No-one was there to take care of her. To pay attention to her, acknowledge her, help her. Everyone just hurried on past. Past her. A woman rummaging in her purse with gloved fingers. Those damn Kleenex, vanished into thin air. The fountain on Grand Army Plaza wasn't even on. But to abandon her walk after not even two blocks just for that? Alright then, just keep sniffing back the snot, cross the street on the next Walk signal and then no more experiments, down Fifth Avenue for a little way and across to Madison. The gray suit had been a mistake. One more mistake, that's all. Yet another. No great surprise. She was forever making mistakes. Nightmare. It hadn't always been that way. It used to be different. She never used to keep screwing up all the time. Always knew exactly what she wanted and how much. Had the knack. Without having to think about it. Thinking had never done her much good anyway. Thinking had never helped her come to any kind of decision. The whole bloody mulling over of things — all it did was give you wrinkles. She'd never thought anything over in her life. Couldn't see the point of it. The fact was she was an intellectual write-off. She simply didn't know a thing. Completely uneducated. She'd never read anything in her life. So what *had* she learned? The different ways of holding your head and what they meant: bowing the head indicated submission, tilting it back the opposite, a slight inclination of the head showed empathy, while a head held high suggested calm and resilience. Amazing that she'd remembered that. Normally she never remembered a thing. Not a clue about anything, but her intuition was spot-on! It was something she used to be able to rely on. Ever since she was a little boy, she'd known what she wanted. In the past, at least. And now it was gone, her darned intuition. Evaporated into thin air. Where the hell was it, her famous intuition, when she forced herself into that monstrosity of a bathing costume? Rushed knowingly towards her downfall, as the camera rolled. Utter suicide. The air was thin at the summit. You only had to look down and you were done for. It was then that the goddamn fear took hold. And then there was nothing left.

Did a runny nose come before or after a blocked nose? What was the normal order of a cold for god's sake? She would call Jane later and ask her. Jane knew stuff like that. Or at least she pretended to, which amounted to the same thing. Although last night she hadn't known what to suggest either. Surely it's O.K. to call a good friend during the night if you're in distress! She'd been in a really bad way. Dumbass thoughts the whole time, crazy dreams. Unbearable. Now it was clear what had been going on: a cold on the way, but last night it could just as easily have been a stroke or rheumatism or cancer. Did nose cancer actually exist? It probably had a different name. But a cold might well lead to sinusitis, judging by the amount of snot. And she hadn't even washed her hair yesterday evening. Why the hell not? Oh, that was it, Cecil, the old charmer, had telephoned yet again and gone on and on. To think she'd even had the call put through! Give him the slightest bit of attention and you soon live to regret it. The old whining sissy was even worse than Mercedes. Nothing but reproaches and declarations of love. No wonder she'd gotten a migraine afterwards. If only she hadn't answered the telephone and had washed her hair instead. Then that would at least be out of the way. Her nose again. It was all so godawful. And now a red light. What the devil was it? A camera, over there, pointing at her. There you go. I thought so. Behind it a woman, a young thing, of the thrusty-busty variety. Which made a change. Oh no, did she just . . . ? Would you believe it! Now she's been snapped blowing her nose. In broad daylight. The cheek of it! Could it get any worse? The photographer was already gone. The street teeming. One helluva crowd. Salvation Army ladies with leaflets and an accordion, the poor soul with his hot-dog cart, the newspaper man behind his pile of nickels and bundles of paper. Everyone had something to do. Everyone except her. She didn't even read the newspaper. It never had anything in it. Well now, who was that honey on the cover of *Life* magazine? Boy, who'd've thought it! Little Monroe, eyelids at half-mast, platinum blonde, shoulders bared – half minx, half deluxe doll, but not without style. She definitely had talent in that department. The "Talk of Hollywood", was she? You don't say. So word had finally got around that the fluffy bunny had what it takes. She'd seen it coming years ago. A hotshot. No, a bombshell. And the perfect choice to play the girl who turns Dorian Gray's head. Heavenly! That would've been it! Monroe as Sybil and she herself as Dorian. Yes, that would've been it, the perfect comeback role. And at some point in the movie, Monroe naked as a jaybird! May as well go the whole hog; anything less would be a waste. That would've been it! The great Garbo, ruined by the little Monroe. A triumph of acting! Goddammit, that would've been it. And she'd known it. Just known it. Only they didn't get it. But they never got anything, those schmucks. Always coming up with those bloody female roles. Dying of true love or some such pathetic nonsense. A corpse from the Seine carving out a career as a death mask with a moronic grin. If you're going for a mask, you may as well do it properly. She'd wanted to play a clown, a male clown who, beneath the make-up and silk pants, is actually a woman. And all his female admirers don't get why he won't reply. But Billy hadn't got it either. A traitor just like all the rest. All the nauseous memories were bubbling back up in her like yesterday's dinner.

To think he'd dared to mention her in the same breath as all those old silent-movie has-beens. As if she were already written off, as if she'd already snuffed it! Just despicable. The truth is there was only one director she would've trusted blind, and he was dead as a doornail. For him she would've happily played a ghost, even a lamppost! He could've done anything he liked with her. Anything! But he didn't want to. He'd liked her, though, that time at Berger's place. And she'd liked him, all sun-tanned as he was. Just back from the South Pacific, tall and lean as ever. Stony broke, but staying at the Miramar with his German shepherd. Wonderfully arrogant and fantastically authoritarian. You never knew quite what he meant by something. The way he'd told her that his family had emigrated from Sweden centuries ago. And stood there all stiff as if that proved something. Simply adorable. But then later, on the pool table, he went all soft. Not surprising, considering how sloshed they both were. His sharp brown eyes, his red hair, his twitchy mouth, that voice rolling on. Her kinda squeeze. But it wasn't to be. Again that was just the beginning of the end. Five weeks later he was dead. Like all the people who'd really meant something to her: Alva, Moje, and then Murr too. They would've been good together. He hadn't been against the idea, at any rate. The fact he was into boys wasn't an obstacle. On the contrary: she'd never been a girl. How Cecil had mocked her about that. "Come on, you were never a boy." But then he'd dug out a photograph of her and seen something, a moment that didn't yet contain all the others that came after. Her gloomy childhood. The goddamn poverty, the ash-gray life on Söder. Father in one corner of the room bent over a newspaper, mother in another, mending clothes. Always a bad atmosphere. Then she did want Cecil to touch her after all. And above all not to let go until she cried *Nicht machen!* Schleesky never touched her. Even though his hands were as big as toilet lids. It was a damn shame.

The window displays of the fashion houses weren't as tasteful as they used to be. Where the devil could she get hold of a mauve carpet? And where was it again that she'd seen that painted furniture? But what's the point? Her apartment would still be boring as hell even with that in it. A shithole with a view of Central Park. There was nothing in it she liked. God, what a nightmare. She would have to move again. A vagabond existence, a life on the run, on the fringes. Always lonely, all on her own-some. Going to bed with the chickens. Theater hardly ever, the movies only when there was no line. There was nothing for her to do. Virgos are said to be good at mending things. But the only thing she was good at was moving apartments. *C'est la vie.* No, it wasn't life. It was her. Cecil was right. She was wasting her best years. If only someone else could live for her, nourish her with their blood. But who could it be? Even Jane's patience had run out last night. Then of all times! And to have the nerve to tally up in front of her the number of times she'd already called! Ten times? So what if she had! First Cecil's grotesque accusations, then the realization that she didn't have an ounce of energy left to wash her hair today. And then Jane's coldness towards her. Cecil, meanwhile, had gotten so clingy, it was just pathetic. Nearly as bad as Mercedes. Except that the old crow brought her bad luck to boot. That chiropractor she'd recommended. Dr Wolf — his very name was a bad omen! She'd only actually had a problem with her wrist. But then he'd gone and started crunching away at her back and her hips as well. He'd pushed her whole bone struc-ture out of place! Once he'd finished, not only were her hips out of joint, her mouth was lopsided as well. He'd almost done her in.

Should she get a coffee? But where? She was already too far downtown. Ah, dammit. Shame she hadn't thought of it sooner! Oh, and she had to go to the health food store! She was meant to go last week to pick up her nettle tea. How could she have forgotten something so important! Typical. So she did have something to do, a destination, after all. The health food store on the corner of Lexington Avenue and 57th Street. She *was* sick, after all. Maybe the funny-looking little brunette would be there. Not exactly a beauty, but so nice and trusting. Everything would be fine. What a marvelous idea. She could let her have some more Kleenex as well, and possibly mix her up a vitamin cocktail. After that she would call Jane and summon her to lunch at Colony's. Give her another chance. Or simply go to the Three Crowns on her own and eat smorgasbord. No deadly dull steamed vegetables, no grilled chicken for once. Afterwards treat herself to a nice whiskey at the Peacock Gallery and smoke her way through a pack of Kent Gold. She could go to the tailor's and have some new pants made to measure. Yes, she could even call Cecil and ask him to track down a sweater in dusty pink. He would probably manage it too. He was so vivacious and so tremendously capable and so terribly interested – in things and in people. So why the devil he wanted to spend time with her was a mystery. She knew better than anyone how unbelievably boring she was. After all, she was the one who had to put up with it the whole time. Couldn't just hang up when it got too much for her. Couldn't get away from herself. Sadly that wasn't an option. Ah, how she'd love to have a break from herself. Be someone else. That was the good thing about all the damn filming. It was handy when there was a script. Schleesky wasn't a particularly gifted writer, of course. But better a bad master than none at all. And there had been a fair few men. Into double digits, certainly. The women didn't count. They were on a different page. Perhaps Cecil was too. She liked him, at any rate. Who else could she say that of? A crime that he hadn't simply grabbed her by the scruff of the neck and led her up the aisle. Instead the fool had waited for a yes. That he hadn't realized she had to be forced into happiness.

That all she needed was a kick up the ass! That she'd simply for-gotten how to say yes. Of course she wanted to make movies. But she was entitled to wait for decent offers. She owed herself that, after that disaster with the bathing costume. It's just it wasn't that easy to judge what was a decent offer. Madame Chichi in "The Magic Mountain"? Marie Curie and her X-rays? Her intu-ition had deserted her. Just like that. And that devoted creep Schleesky, sure, he was good at getting her a car and a bottle of vodka in the middle of the night, but where roles were concerned he was anything but helpful. He was a bloody tyrant, obviously. That was the glorious thing about him. For a small man he had very big hands. He could order everyone around with them. Without even raising his voice. And everyone was shit-scared of him. A Cerberos or Cerberus, or whatever its name was. But someone who at least knew what he wanted. The way he looked at her sometimes. With cold fish-eyes, as if she wasn't even there.

There it was now, next to the automat. Her destination, her lighthouse, her beloved health food store. And she was in luck. The little brunette was there. And she already had the tea in her hand. You could count on her. The white coat really suited her as she leaned forward. But why the strange expression on her face? "My goodness, Miss Garbo, you don't look at all well." What the hell? "What? Have I changed that much?" A look of horror. "No, no, not at all." Now she was playing it down, trying to erase what had been said. But she knew what she'd heard. Oh God, she had to get out of here right away. Take the tea. It was already paid for anyway. And out. What a nightmare. Shit. She obviously looked a wreck. Worse than usual anyhow. She had to see for herself. Where, though? A mirror in the store window. Shit. What a sight! It was true, she looked hideous, just awful. Red eyes, red nose, wrinkles, more of them than ever before. Her neck all saggy. Lines everywhere that would be wrinkles in no time. Furrows, more like,

deep crevices around her mouth from the goddamn smoking.
Ones that no mask-maker could disguise. The marble was crumbling. The firm contours she still had would soften and be gradually lost. The role of the death mask would've suited her well. If
you died young you at least had that consolation. She'd actually
kept Murr's mask.

The lengths she'd gone to for this face. Had her hairline
straightened, her teeth fixed, her hairstyle and hair color changed.
No wonder the bastards imagined it belonged to them. She only
need blink an eye and the whole world was interpreting it. Her
smile, mysterious. Her eyes, prophetic. Her cheekbones, divine.
What complete bullshit. Adoration always spelled the beginning
of the end. After that you just became an effigy or a martyr. Christ.
So much for goddess. A tarted-up ass, that's what she'd been all
these years. Somebody'd missed a good man in her. Nice and
tall with broad shoulders, huge hands and feet. But they didn't
want that body. In fact they'd taken to their heels when they'd
seen it half-naked. An oversized pedestal, a support system for
this goddamn face of hers! That was her true enemy. So much
for marble. Nothing but a mask, an empty vessel. They were so
hell-bent on finding out what was behind it. Nothing was behind
it. Nothing!

But now it occurred to her: it wasn't the bathing suit! That
hadn't been the problem, as she'd always thought. It wasn't the
bathing suit but the damn bathing cap! That blasted strap under
her chin which left an imprint on her skin. Her flesh was already
soft there, a little bit slack. Aging started early. Basically at birth.
It was all too late now anyway. To hell with it! Who cares. A
cigarette would be good now. Bring them on, those little sticks
of death! Father always used to say tomorrow will be better. And
then he'd died. The last ten years had been difficult enough. The
next ten would just be horrendous. She was so tired of everything.

Even tired of being tired. Others had husbands, children or memories. She had nothing besides her accursed fame and her lousy money that condemned her to not having to go to work on a Monday in April, to some office downtown, to some dusty studio in Culver City, to anywhere. The truth was her life was over. So much for a woman with a past. A woman without a future, that's what she was. A rudderless ship, always alone. Poor little Garbo! A hopeless case. Once a crowd puller, now a stray dog roaming the streets of Manhattan day in, day out, that cesspool of a city that reeked of trash even in April. But where the hell was she meant to go? Her face was known the world over. She could hide under a fishing hat or wrap herself in a full-length seal-fur coat, it made no difference; sooner or later she was discovered. There were vultures everywhere. It was only ever a matter of time. No, she was glad it was over. That it had been her decision. The time comes when you have more to lose than to gain. She'd worked hard. Never used to have any time. Well she had plenty now, just not the foggiest fart what to do with it. The East River was too filthy for anyone to want to drown themselves in it. A lot of women lost their mind. Not her, unfortunately. She just got sick. Or perhaps she'd been crazy for ages and simply hadn't noticed. Or dead even? Who knows, maybe for years now. Had she ever even been young? She couldn't remember. She could never remember anything. Except the sense of having already seen and experienced everything: the mountains of mail, the hum of the spotlights, the flash-guns, the whole damn circus. Los Angeles was one long nightmare. There was no place on earth more boring. A godforsaken city without sidewalks. For crying out loud! How often had she had her chauffeur drive her the five hours up to Santa Barbara, just to have a bit of a stroll around, only to realize that she couldn't stop for a cup of tea anywhere there either. That there too the hounds were lying in wait everywhere.

All she wanted was to be left in peace. But how come she had no-one to take care of her? How come she didn't have a husband and children? All the people she loved died. And the ones who still admired her were old. As old as she was. She should've done like Murr. Sold everything and disappeared for good. It didn't necessarily need to be the South Pacific. It was coming back that spelled the end for him. A truck coming in the opposite direction, an embankment. All the others were uninjured, the chauffeur and the little Filipino who'd been at the wheel. The German shepherd had just run off. It was probably still roaming the valley to this day. The back of Murr's lovely head completely crushed. There was no sign of that, though, when he lay there in the funeral parlor, in his gray suit, his proud, noble face plastered with gaudy make-up like some old Berlin faggot. A stick-thin, dolled-up corpse surrounded by wreaths and crosses crafted from gardenias. Here, even the dead were made up as if for technicolor. And all around, masses of empty garden chairs with those waxy, brightly patterned chintz cushions, which no-one wanted to sit on. Only a handful of old fools turned up anyway. The last of the faithful. Fire or earth, that was the question. She hadn't even made up her mind on that. Ah, what she would give to be able to turn back the clock! And rather than missing the boat, to get married or even make another movie! She'd wanted to, after all! She'd even done screen tests. She'd recited her lines nicely in La Brea, the wind in her hair from the machine. Weren't they all delighted? And hadn't James said to her, "Miss Garbo, you're still the world's most beautiful woman?" And he really meant it. That wasn't even all that long ago. Two or three years. So close. What was it again? A duchess who was unlucky in love and became a nun. Whatever. She was living the life of a nun now anyway. Although it had been nice with Cecil. Queers were simply better lovers. The way he'd grabbed her by the hair and pulled until it hurt. Sometimes he just knew what she needed. She'd come so close. She'd have played any old nonsense. She'd worked her ass off, even done upper arm workouts. But no, whenever she thought it was about to happen, something got in the way. It was like she was jinxed! Schleesky was always saying she was like Duse. She'd hidden herself away for eleven whole years too, and then returned to the stage. Notched up triumphs like never before. What year were they now again? 1952, dammit. So her eleven years were up. It was eleven lousy years since all the world had seen her in the pool and laughed at her. And now, what was she now? A woman with nothing to wear. An out-of-work actress. A living fossil. A ghost who wandered around midtown in broad daylight on the look-out for dusty-pink cashmere sweaters and some kind of meaning! A zombie, buried alive in these ravines, these dreary straight streets of towering red-brick buildings. To think of all the things she'd tried! Astrology, theosophy, even psychoanalysis – with Dr Gräsberg, the only Swedish psychoanalyst in the whole of West Hollywood. How he told her after a few weeks that she was suffering from narcissistic personality disorder. Genius! And as she walked out, there was that poster of her plastered above the highway, larger than life. With that, how could you *not* have a disorder? She'd never gone back. In any case she didn't like to see her soul laid bare. In fact, Cecil doubted she even had one. He was probably right. She was probably really just a bad person. Yes, that's what she was: a bad person with bad manners. She wouldn't change now. Had he ever really believed she could play his wife? An offer of a part, all the same. Her last one. Now it was too late for anything. How long had she been old, though? It couldn't be that long. When had it started, this blasted aging? When she started getting excited about the spring. In the past it had always left her cold. She only used to miss the winter. That single withered dead tree in the backyard of her apartment on San

Vicente Boulevard, her winter tree. How often had she imagined that the cold had made it leafless, and that soon there would be snow on its branches. But of course it never came. How could it? In friggin' California! Instead what you got was the rain after Christmas, when it pissed down until the canyon overflowed. You could leave everything behind: your parents, your language, your nationality, just not the climate of your childhood. But then: roses blooming in April, the sweet scent of orange blossom. The damp, foggy days in Mabery Road, mornings on the beach, the only place you could go for a walk. In the end, all her attempts to get away were defeated by the climate. And where had she wound up? In this crummy city that stank of formaldehyde, sweat and garbage. When she came here for the first time she'd been a youngster, still wet behind the ears. It was summer, so scorching hot that you couldn't go out. She thought she would die. At night she didn't get a wink of sleep because of the noise of the garbage being crushed in the yard. Just lay there listening to the vile chomping of the infernal machine, the sirens of the fire trucks, the honking of the cars, that nerve-shattering din. She could've happily drowned herself in the bath, only the room didn't have one. And now? Now this hole of a city was the only home she still had. She wasn't dead. The dead didn't catch colds, as far as she knew. No, she was alive. She was still alive. And that was the problem. California then? Or Europe after all? Staying here wasn't an option. Perhaps start small. One step at a time. First go home, make tea, call Jane, wash her hair. Then maybe California. With a detour to Palm Springs. Then in summer over to Europe. Nice is supposed to be such a lovely island.

Lesbos
THE LOVE SONGS OF SAPPHO

* *The songs of Sappho were composed during Greece's Archaic period in around 600 B.C. on the island of Lesbos in the eastern Aegean.*

† *Although Sappho's songs were probably written down immediately after her death on Lesbos in such a way that they could be performed again, nothing remains of the notation of the musical accompaniment. It may already have been lost long before Alexandrian scholars in the third and second centuries before Christ published her known work, which at the time was split between various Athenian editions and anthologies, in complete editions with critical commentaries. A comment by Philodemus of Gadara from the first century suggests that, in his day, hetaerae would sing Sappho's songs at banquets and during love play.*

Her poetry is presumed to have been lost at some point during the Byzantine era — by an effective combination of sheer neglect and wilful destruction. The philosopher Michael Italicus, writing in the first half of the twelfth century, refers to Sappho in a way that implies he was familiar with her work. Yet the scholar John Tzetzes, writing around the same time, mentions that her poems are lost. Some believe they were burned in the year 1073 under Pope Gregory VII or obliterated in the sack of Constantinople in the Fourth Crusade in 1204; others speculate that her texts were destroyed on the orders of Bishop Gregory of Nazianzus back at the end of the fourth century, while still others hold that it must have been even earlier, as her poems were not quoted by any of the later grammarians.

Studies of numerous albeit fragmentary papyri have uncovered a considerable number of additional texts in recent years.

As Nebuchadnezzar II is plundering Jerusalem, Solon ruling
Athens, Phoenician seafarers circumnavigating the African continent for the first time and Anaximander postulating that an
indefinite primal matter is the origin of all things and that the
soul is air-like in nature, Sappho writes:

> He seems to me equal to the gods that man
> whoever he is who opposite you
> sits and listens close
>   to your sweet speaking
>
> and lovely laughing – oh it
> puts the heart in my chest on wings
> for when I look at you, even a moment, no speaking
>   is left in me
>
> no: tongue breaks and thin
> fire is racing under skin
> and in eyes no sight and drumming
>   fills ears
>
> and cold sweat holds me and shaking
> grips me all, greener than grass
> I am and dead – or almost
>   I seem to me.
>
> But all is to be dared, because even a person of poverty . . .

Buddha and Confucius are not yet born, the idea of democracy
and the word "philosophy" not yet conceived, but Eros – Aphrodite's servant – already rules with an unyielding hand: as a god,
one of the oldest and most powerful, but also as an illness with

unclear symptoms that assails you out of the blue, a force of nature that descends on you, a storm that whips up the sea and uproots even oak trees, a wild, uncontrollable beast that suddenly pounces on you, unleashes unbridled pleasure and causes unspeakable agonies – bittersweet, consuming passion.

There are not many surviving literary works older than the songs of Sappho: the down-to-earth Epic of Gilgamesh, the first ethereal hymns of the Rigveda, the inexhaustible epic poems of Homer and the many-stranded myths of Hesiod, in which it is written that the Muses know everything. "They know all that has been, is and will be." Their father is Zeus, their mother Mnemosyne, a Titaness, the goddess of memory.

We know nothing. Not much, at any rate. Not even whether Homer really existed, or the identity of that author whom we for the sake of convenience have dubbed "Pseudo-Longinus", who quotes Sappho's verses on the power of Eros in the surviving fragments of his work on the sublime, thereby preserving her lines for future generations, namely us.

We know that Sappho came from Lesbos, an island in the eastern Aegean situated so close to the mainland of Asia Minor that, on a clear day, you might think you could swim across – to the coast of the immeasurably rich Lydia of those days, and from there, in what is now Turkey, to that of the immeasurably rich Europe of today.

Somewhere there, in the lost kingdom of the Hittites, must lie the origins of her unusual name, which either means "numinous", "clean" or "pure source", or – if you trace its history back by a different route – is a corruption of the ancient Greek word for sapphire and lapis lazuli.

She is said to have been born in Eresus, or perhaps in Mytilene, in about the year 617 before our calendar began, or possibly thirteen years earlier or five years later. Her father was called Scamander or Scamandronymus, or otherwise possibly Simon, Eumenus, Eerigyius, Ecrytus, Semus, Camon or Etarchus, according to the Suda, a highly eloquent but not very reliable Byzantine encyclopaedia from the tenth century.

We know she had two brothers named Charaxus and Larichus, and perhaps a third named Eurygius, and that she was of noble birth, since her youngest brother Larichus was a cup-bearer in the Prytaneion in Mytilene, a post reserved only for the sons of aristocratic families.

We believe her mother was called Cleïs and that Sappho had a daughter of the same name, even though the word, which she uses when addressing the beloved girl in a poem, can also mean slave.

Nowhere does Sappho refer to a husband. The name "Kerkylas of Andros Island" mentioned in this connection in the Suda has to be a smutty joke by the Attic comic poets, who undoubtedly took pleasure in ascribing to her, of all women, a husband with a name sometimes rendered as "Dick Allcock from the Isle of Man". The legend of her unhappy, even self-destructive love for a young ferryman named Phaeon, later embellished by Ovid in his *Letters of Heroines*, must date from the same time.

We know from an inscribed chronicle dating from the third century before Christ that at some point – when exactly is not recorded on the Parian marble tablet – she fled by ship to Syracuse. We can conclude from another source that it was in around 596 B.C., when Lesbos' fortunes were in the hands of the Cleanactidai clan.

Seven or eight years later, when the island was under the rule of the tyrant Pittacus, she must have returned from exile and founded a women's circle in Mytilene, which may have been a cultish community set up to honour Aphrodite, a symposium of fellow females bearing an erotic attachment to one another, or a marriage preparation school for daughters of noble birth: no-one knows for sure.

No other woman from early antiquity has been so talked about, and in such conflicting terms. The sources are as sparse as the legends are manifold, and any attempt to distinguish between the two virtually hopeless.

Every age has created its own Sappho. Some even invented a second in order to sidestep the contradictions of the stories: she was variously described as a priestess in the service of Aphrodite or the Muses, a hetaera, a man-crazed woman, a love-crazed virago, a kindly teacher, a gallant lady; by turns shameless and corrupt, or prim and pure.

Her fellow countryman and contemporary Alcaeus described her as "violet-haired, pure, honey-smiling", Socrates as "beautiful", Plato as "wise", Philodemus of Gadara as "the tenth Muse", Strabo as "a marvellous phenomenon" and Horace as "masculine", but there is now no way of knowing what exactly he meant by that.

A papyrus from the late second or early third century for its part claims that Sappho was "ugly, being dark in complexion and of very small stature", "contemptible" and "a woman-lover".

At one time bronze statues of her were common; even today, silver coins still bear her laurel-crowned profile, a water jug from the school of Polygnotos portrays her as a slim figure reading a scroll, and a gleaming black vase from the fifth century before

Christ shows her as tall in stature, holding an eight-stringed lyre in her hand as if she had just finished playing or were just about to start.

We do not know how Sappho's verses sounded in Aeolic – the most archaic and tricky of the extinct ancient Greek dialects, in which the initial aspiration was omitted from words – when they were sung at a wedding ceremony, at a banquet or in the women's circle, accompanied by a stringed instrument: the hushed sound of a plucked phorminx or the festive ring of the cithara, the deep tones of the barbitos or the harp-like strains of the pectis, the high tones of a magadis or the dull resonance of a tortoise-shell lyre.

All we know is that the word "lyric" derives from one of these instruments, the lyre, and was coined by Alexandrian scholars some three hundred years after Sappho's death. It was they who dedicated to her an entire edition in eight or nine books, many thousands of lines on several rolls of papyrus, arranged according to metre, several hundred poems, of which only a single one has come to us intact, because the rhetorician Dionysius of Halicarnassus, who lived in Rome during the reign of Augustus, quotes it in full in his treatise *On Literary Composition* as an example worthy of admiration. Other than that, four consecutive stanzas were recorded by the scholar known as Pseudo-Longinus; five stanzas of another poem were successfully reassembled from three different papyrus fragments; four stanzas of another were discovered in 1937 carelessly scrawled on a palm-sized potsherd by an Egyptian schoolboy in the second century before Christ; fragments of a fifth and a sixth poem were preserved on a tattered early mediaeval parchment, and large portions of a seventh and eighth were recently discovered on strips of papyrus forming part

of the cartonnages used for the preservation of Egyptian mum-
mies or as book covers, although the deciphering of one of the
two poems still divides the throng of experts to this day.

A handful of words or isolated lines cited by grammarians like
Athenaeus and Apollonius Dyscolus, the philosopher Chrysippus
of Soli or the lexicographer Julius Pollux to illustrate a certain
style, a particular item of vocabulary or the metre named after her,
were provided by the large-format codices of mediaeval scribes —
the rest is nothing more than scraps: a scattering of stanzas one or
two lines long, fragmentary verses, words plucked from their
context, single syllables and letters, the beginning or end of a
word, or a line, nowhere near a sentence, let alone a meaning.

> ....
> and I go ...
> ...
> ... immediately ...
> ......
> ... for ...
> ... of harmony ...
> ... the chorus, ...
> ... clear-sounding
> ...
> ... to all ...
> ...

It is as if, in the places where the singing has faded away and the
words are missing, where the papyrus scrolls are rotten and torn,
dots had appeared, first singly, then in pairs, and soon in the
vague pattern of a rhythmic triad — the notation of a silent lament.

These songs have fallen silent, turned to writing, Greek characters borrowed from the Phoenician: dark majuscules, carved into clayey earthenware in a clumsy schoolboy hand or copied onto the pith of the woody wetland grass by a diligent professional using a reed pen; and delicate minuscules, written on the pumice-smoothed, chalk-bleached skins of young sheep and stillborn goats: papyrus and parchment, organic materials which, once exposed to the elements, eventually decompose like any cadaver.

> ...
> ... nor ...
> ... desire ...
> ... but all at once ...
> ... blossom ...
> ... desire ...
> ... took delight ...

Like forms to be filled in, these mutilated poems demand to be completed – by interpretation and imagination, or by the deciphering of more of the loose papyrus remnants from the rubbish dumps of Oxyrhynchus, that sunken town in central Egypt where a metre-thick layer of dry sand preserved these rock-hard, worm-eaten fragments – fragile, creased and tattered from being rolled and unrolled – for nearly one thousand years.

We know that people wrote on papyrus scrolls in tightly packed columns without spaces between words, punctuation or guidelines, making even well-preserved items hard to decipher. *Divinatio*, in the ancient art of the oracle, was the gift of prophesying the future by observing bird migrations and interpreting dreams. Nowadays, in papyrology, it refers to the ability to read a line where all that is visible are faded fragments of ancient Greek letters.

The fragment, we know, is the infinite promise of Romanticism, the enduringly potent ideal of the modern age, and poetry, more than any other literary form, has come to be associated with the pregnant void, the blank space that breeds conjecture. The dots, like phantom limbs, seem intertwined with the words, testify to a lost whole. Intact, Sappho's poems would be as alien to us as the once gaudily painted classical sculptures.

In total, all the poems and fragments that have reached us, as brief, mutilated and devoid of context as they are, add up to no more than six hundred lines. It has been calculated that around 7 per cent of Sappho's work has survived.

It has also been calculated that around 7 per cent of all women feel attracted solely or predominantly to women, but no calculation will ever be able to establish whether there is any correlation here.

The history of symbols contains a number of markers of the unknown and indeterminate, of the absent and lost, of the void and the blank: the zero on the corn lists of the ancient Babylonians, the letter x in an algebraic equation, the dash used when someone's words are abruptly interrupted.

> ...   .
> goatherd   longing   sweat
> ...   .
> ... roses ...
> ...

Aposiopesis – the technique of suddenly breaking off mid-sentence – we know is a rhetorical device which Pseudo-Longinus, too, will certainly have written about in that part of his treatise *On the*

Sublime that has been lost owing to the carelessness of librarians and bookbinders. If someone stops speaking, starts stuttering and stammering or even falls silent, it suggests he is overcome by feelings of such magnitude that inevitably words fail him. Ellipses open up any text to that vast obscure realm of sentiments that cannot be verbalised or that capitulate in the face of the words available.

> ... my darling one ...

We know that the letters Emily Dickinson wrote to her friend and future sister-in-law Susan Gilbert had a series of passionate passages deleted from them, prior to publication, by her niece Martha, Gilbert's daughter, who omitted to indicate these deletions. One of these censored sentences from June 11, 1852 reads: "If you were here – and Oh that you were here, my Susie, we need not talk at all, our eyes would whisper for us, and your hand fast in mine, we would not ask for language."

Wordless, blind understanding is as much a firm topos of love poetry as is the wordy evocation of unfathomable feeling.

Sappho's words, where decipherable, are as unambiguous and clear as words possibly can be. At once sober and passionate, they tell, in an extinct language which has to be resurrected with each translation, of a heavenly power that, twenty-six centuries on, has lost none of its might: the sudden transformation, as wondrous as it is merciless, of a person into an object of desire, rendering you defenceless and causing you to leave your parents, spouse and even children.

> Eros the melter of limbs (now again) stirs me –
> sweetbitter unmanageable creature who steals in

We know that the categorisation of desire according to whether its protagonists were of the same or different genders was a concept foreign to the ancient Greeks. Rather, what mattered to them was that, in sexual relations, the role of each of the persons involved mirrored their social one, with adult men taking an active sexual role, while youths, slaves and women remained passive. The dividing line in this act of control and submission ran not between the sexes, but between those who penetrate and possess, and those who are penetrated and possessed.

Men are not mentioned by name in the surviving poetry of Sappho, whereas many women are: Abanthis, Agallis, Anagora, Anactoria, Archeanassa, Arignota, Atthis, Cleïs, Cleanthis, Dica, Doricha, Eirana, Euneica, Gongyla, Gorgo, Gyrinna, Megara, Mica, Mnasis, Mnasidica, Pleistodica, Telesippa. It is they whom Sappho sings about, with tender devotion or flaming desire, with burning jealousy or icy contempt.

> Someone will remember us
> I say
>   even in another time

We think we know that Sappho was a teacher, even though the first source to refer to her as such is a papyrus fragment dating from the second century A.D., which reports, seven hundred years after her death, that she had taught girls from the best families in Ionia and Lydia.

There is nothing in any of Sappho's surviving poetry to suggest an educational setting, although the fragments contain descriptions of a world in which women come and go, and there is often mention of farewells. The place seems to be one of transition, which led some to interpret it as hosting the female equivalent of the more widely attested Greek practice of paederasty. This reading also conveniently enabled the undeniable presence of female eroticism in poetry to be accounted for as a form of preparation for the main focus, the undisputed culmination of that teaching, namely marriage.

We do not know the exact nature of the relationship between Hannah Wright and Anne Gaskill, whose marriage was recorded without comment in the Register of Marriages of the parish of Taxal in northern England on September 4, 1707, though we do know that the expression "Where you go I will go" commonly used in Christian marriage ceremonies is borrowed from the words spoken by the widowed Ruth to her mother-in-law Naomi in the Old Testament.

We also know that in 1819, in the court case involving the two headmistresses of a Scottish girls' boarding school who – a pupil had alleged – had engaged in improper and criminal acts on one another, Lucian's *Dialogues of the Hetaerae* was quoted to show that sex between women was actually possible. In it the hetaera Clonarion asks the cithara player Leaina about her sexual experience with "a rich woman from Lesbos" and in particular presses her to reveal what exactly she had done with her and "using what method". But Leaina counters: "Don't question me too closely about these things, they're shameful; so, by Aphrodite, I won't tell you!"

The chapter ends at this point, the question goes unanswered, and so what women do with one another remains both unuttered and unutterable. At any rate the two teachers were acquitted of the charge, as the judge came to the conclusion that the transgression of which they were accused was not actually possible:

Where there is no instrument there can be no act, where there is no weapon there can be no crime.

For a long time, what women do with one another could only be regarded as sex and therefore an offence if it mimicked sexual intercourse between a man and a woman. The phallus marked the sexual act, and where it was absent there was nothing but an unmarked blank, a blind spot, a gap, a hole to be filled like the female sexual organ.

For a long time, this empty place was occupied by the concept of the "tribade", that spectre that haunts the writings of men, namely a masculine-acting woman who had sex with other women with the help of a monstrously enlarged clitoris or a phallic aid. As far as we know, no woman has ever described herself as a tribade.

We know that words and symbols change their meaning. For a long time, three dots in a row along the writing baseline designated something lost and unknown, then at some point also something unuttered and unutterable; no longer only something omitted or left out, but also something left open. Hence the three dots became a symbol that invites one to think the allusion to its conclusion, imagine that which is missing, a proxy for the inexpressible and the hushed-up, for the offensive and obscene, for the incriminating and speculative, for a particular version of the omitted: the truth.

We also know that in ancient times the symbol for omissions was the asterisk – the little star that only in mediaeval times took on the task of linking a place in a text to its associated margin note. As Isidore of Seville writes in the seventh century in his *Etymologies*: "The asterisk is placed next to omissions, so that things which appear to be missing may be clarified through this mark."

Nowadays the asterisk is sometimes used as a means of including as many people as possible and their sexual identities. The omission becomes an inclusion, the absence a presence, and the empty place a profusion of meaning.

And we know that in ancient times the verb *lesbiazein*, "to do it like women from Lesbos", was used to mean "to violate or corrupt somebody", and to refer to the sexual practice of fellatio, which was assumed to have been invented by the women of the island of Lesbos. Even Erasmus of Rotterdam, in his collection of ancient sayings and expressions, renders the Greek word as the Latin *fellare*, meaning "to suck", and concludes the entry with the comment: "The term remains, but I think the practice has been eliminated."

Not long after that, at the end of the sixteenth century, Pierre de Bourdeille, seigneur de Brantôme, comments in his pornographic novel *The Lives of the Gallant Ladies*: "'Tis said how that Sappho the Lesbian was a very high mistress in this art, and that in after times the Lesbian dames have copied her therein, and continued the practice to the present day." From then on the empty space had not only a geographical but also a linguistic home, although the term *amour lesbien* remained in common use until the modern age as a term describing the unrequited love of a woman for a younger man.

We know that the two young poetesses Natalie Clifford Barney and Renée Vivien were disappointed when, in late summer 1904, they fulfilled a long-cherished dream and visited the isle of Lesbos together. When they finally reached the port of Mytilene, French chansons were blaring from a phonograph, and both the visual appearance of the island's female inhabitants and the crudeness of their idiom were at odds with the poetesses' noble imaginings of this place so frequently evoked in their own poems. Nevertheless, they rented two neighbouring villas in an olive grove, went for long moonlit and sunlit walks, rekindled their love that had grown cold some years earlier and talked about setting up a school of lesbian poetry and love on the island.

The idyll ended when a third woman – a jealous and possessive baroness with whom Vivien was in a liaison – announced she was on her way, and a telegram had to be sent to stop her. Barney and Vivien separated. Back in Paris, their mutual Ancient Greek teacher served from then on as the bearer of their secret letters.

We know that, in 2008, two female residents and one male resident of the island of Lesbos unsuccessfully attempted to introduce a ban on women not originally from the island naming themselves after it or being named after it by others: "We object to the arbitrary use of the name of our homeland by persons of sexual deviation." The presiding judge rejected the application and ordered the three Lesbians to bear the court costs.

Who, these days, is still familiar with the "Lesbian rule" alluded to by Aristotle in his *Nicomachean Ethics*, used in cases where general laws cannot be applied to concrete situations, following the example of the master builders of Lesbos, who used a leaden rule that "can be bent to the shape of the stone", since it was better, in a concrete situation, to have a crooked but functioning rule than to follow an ideal which is smooth and straight but useless.

And who, these days, is still familiar with the Sapphic stanza, that four-line verse form comprising three hendecasyllabic lines of matching structure, consisting of trochees with a dactyl inserted in third place, and an adonic as the fourth line, in which each line starts directly with a stressed syllable, every line ending is feminine, and the solemn dignity so characteristic of this metre yields at the end to a sense of reassurance or even serenity.

For a long time terms like "tribadism", "Sapphism" and "lesbian-ism" were used more or less synonymously in the treatises of theologians, jurists and physicians, though in some instances they denoted a perverse sexual practice or shameless custom, and in others a monstrous anomaly or mental illness.

We do not know exactly why the term "lesbian love" has endured for some time now, only that this expression and its associations will fade in the same way as all its predecessors.

L is an apical consonant, E the vowel expelled most directly, S is a hissing, warning sound, B an explosive sound that blasts the lips apart . . .

In German dictionaries, "*lesbisch*" ("lesbian") comes immediately after "*lesbar*" ("legible").

Behrenhoff
THE VON BEHR PALACE

* *From the fourteenth century, the Gützkow branch of the old von Behr family, also known as the "Swans' Necks" in reference to the motif on their coat of arms, owned a large amount of land in the area in Pomerania known as Busdorf, near Greifswald.*

In 1804, with the approval of the Swedish-Pomeranian government in Stralsund, the place was renamed "Behrenhoff", and cavalry captain Johann Carl Ulrich von Behr turned the farm estate into an entail in favour of his grandson Carl Felix Georg, with the stipulation that primogeniture should always apply in event of its inheritance.

The latter had a new, two-storey mansion built behind the old farmhouse in the late classical style based on plans by Friedrich Hitzig, a pupil of Schinkel, which was completed in 1838. In 1896 the building was extended by Carl Felix Woldemar, who had been elevated to the Prussian rank of count in 1877, and the two single-storey verandas enlarged, with another storey added on top. From 1936 to 1939, Countess Mechthild von Behr, widow of the last count, the Imperial District Administrator and longstanding member of parliament Carl Friedrich Felix von Behr, who died in 1933, placed the mansion at the disposal of the Confessing Church as a lecture venue. The theologian Dietrich Bonhoeffer is said to have been a guest there on several occasions.

† *On May 8, 1945 the mansion went up in flames. The burned-out ruins were used by the local residents as a source of building materials for new farmhouses.*

The nine-hectare landscaped park designed by Peter Joseph Lenné and laid out between 1840 and 1860 today has protected status.

I remember the open window. It is night, and the air is cool. An open window on a summer's night. No moon in the sky. Only the diffuse light of the street lamp. It smells of earth. Perhaps it has rained. I cannot remember.

It was July 31, says my mother. She is quite certain, because July 31 is Tante Kerstin's birthday, and that evening she was having a celebration in one of the old estate workers' cottages opposite. It definitely didn't rain, she adds. It was a fine day. Sunny the whole day. As you'd expect in July.

The weather records also show that it was a hot day, indeed that the whole summer was warm and exceptionally dry.

Summer 1984. It is my earliest memory: this I know, I think, I claim. I could telephone Tante Kerstin. She is still alive. As are my mother and both my fathers. The one who conceived me, and the one who, later that night, would cool my legs with ice and wrap them in gauze bandages.

I play in the cemetery between the mounds overrun with greenery. I hide behind the graves and headstones, I crouch between plants with tiny blue and white flowers. An elderly woman, shrunken from stooping, throws wilted blooms and dried-out wreaths onto the compost. She holds a tin watering can under the rusty water tap then disappears behind the box hedges.

I duck down, run my fingers over the smooth stone, feel the rough indentations of the chiselled letters and wait for the improbable. I wait to be found. I want to be found. I'm afraid of it.

Throughout my childhood we lived in villages, in rural localities that gave little hint of their more glamorous past. Then, too, we were living in a village, just a few steps from its one and only bus stop, on the first floor of the old verger's house next door to the towerless church with its high stone chancel. Our backyard was directly adjacent to the cemetery. Not even a fence separated the two compost heaps. In my memory, I was almost always alone. Alone in the graveyard, alone in the orchard surrounded by high red walls, alone on the heap of stones which, according to my mother, I kept jumping from on that day.

But no-one came; the miracle, as always, failed to materialise. Instead I picked a few flowers from the little flower beds, plucked pansies out of the ground and extracted single tulips from their pointy plastic vases stuck in the earth.

I had some kind of inkling, but I did not know. Not, at least, that the flowers belonged to the absent, to the dead rotting in wooden boxes beneath the earth. When I took the posy home, my mother was cross and did not explain why.

I had no knowledge of death as yet. That people die, that I myself would one day die, lay beyond my imagination. When, some time later, my cousin let me in on this secret, I did not believe him. I was certain he had overheard something and misunderstood it, as he often did. He grinned. He was sure of himself.

I felt dizzy. I raced through the new-build flat that was our home at the time, into the kitchen and asked my mother whether it was true that people really died, whether we would all die one day, in other words, me included. She nodded, said yes and shrugged her shoulders. I looked at the rubbish bin and, for some reason, imagined that the dead ended up in this container, as shrivelled beings, to be carted off by the refuse collectors. I clamped my hands over my ears, even though no-one was speaking now, and ran into the hallway. Yellow light was shining through the

ridged glass of the window onto the dusty green plants in the
stairwell.

I keep my eyes closed on the ghost train at the funfair in a neighbouring village. My parents let me go on it. Two of their pupils sit
to the left and right of me, a boy and a girl.

As we plunge into the darkness, I cross my arms in front of
my face. A cool draught brushes my skin. I hear a clattering, the
jolting and rolling of the car, a scream. I feel the skin of my eyelids, squeeze my eyes even more tightly shut, hold my breath for
a moment, hum and wait. An eternity goes by.

At some point someone taps me on the shoulder. My mother's
voice says: It's over. I open my eyes. We are back outside. I kept
my eyes closed the whole time, I say proudly. I cheated it. I
cheated fear. What a waste of money, says my mother and lifts me
out of the car.

I play in the garden among the apple trees. I pick masses of
buttercups and stain my fingers with dandelion juice. By the
compost heap I discover a spiky ball. It is breathing. It is alive.

When my mother sets a saucer of milk in front of the ball, it
transforms into a wondrous creature. We crouch down. Black
button eyes look at me. I feel my mother's hand on my head. A
pointy nose sniffs out the milk. A tiny pink tongue darts out. The
animal grunts and slurps. Its prickles bob up and down.

I enjoyed life. I was expecting nothing. My mother was expecting
a baby. But I have no memory of a rounded belly or a man's hand
stroking its curves. She must have been pregnant, the dates tell
me. She was pregnant, the photographs show. One month after
that July night which cannot have been cool, my brother would
be born and my grandmother, having taken the telephone call

from the hospital, would stand in the bedroom doorway in her midnight-blue dressing gown and speak his name for the first time.

I sat there in my grandparents' bed, heard the name, which meant nothing to me, and turned back to the lipsticks, an astonishing collection of small shiny cylinders which my grandmother kept in a case above the bed.

The bedroom window is open, but the door of the flat is closed and locked, and the key is not hanging on the keyholder or lying on the kitchen table. I have woken up and climbed out of my cot. I have opened the bedroom door and searched the whole flat. All the rooms are dark, all the other windows closed: the semi-circular dormer window in the living room, the skylight in the kitchen and the jet-black hole of the windowless boxroom which my father has turned into a small workshop.

There were no other rooms. The bathroom was downstairs on the ground floor. We shared it with Tante Viola from the top-floor flat. We shared the loo, the roaring boiler, the four-footed bath-tub and the raffia mat in front of it. Tante Viola worked in the school canteen in the old stables at the north end of the grounds, a yellow brick building with a stone horse's head looking down from either side of the entrance gate. Where once horses ate their hay, we now had our midday meal. We stood in long queues, the kindergarten children, the school pupils, the teachers, half the village. Tante Viola had bleached blonde hair, purple eye make-up and a lorry driver for a husband, who came home on Saturdays and left again on Sundays, a large faceless figure. The school was behind the grounds, two new buildings with long rows of windows. My parents and also Tante Kerstin taught there. The grounds were large and belonged to the palace that no longer existed. Neither Tante Kerstin nor Tante Viola was a real aunt. We just called them that.

The palace was not a real palace either. It was a mansion, an elongated two-storey building, the centre of the estate, with, next to it, a stable block, a sheep shed, a cattle shed as well as an outbuilding and two barns. An avenue of lime trees led directly to it from the Bear Gate on the village high street, through the northern part of the grounds, which was out of bounds for villagers. My kindergarten stood on what would once have been the generous front drive, a grass-centred circle in front of an open portal that also served as a porch, surmounted by a balcony supported by eight pillars, with triangular gables over the windows, and Virginia creeper growing up the façade.

The window is open; the door of the flat is locked and bolted. My arm stretches up, reaches for the door handle, grips it, pulls it downwards – but the door stays closed.

I remember the big wall cabinet in the living room, the toys lying around by the stove, the rocking chair in suspended motion, an oversized, tidy dolls' house. Only the bedroom window is open and the air outside cool.

The church was in the middle of the village, but everyone just walked on by. Nobody looked over the red brick wall, nobody glanced at the graves and crosses. Only a few stooped old women ever ventured through the creaking gate into the graveyard. We lived right next to the church. But none of it meant anything. Not the huge edifice of hewn granite and rough stone, not the vicarage diagonally opposite, not the wooden bell cage down at ground level, not the bell-ringing on Sundays, not the lopsided rusty crosses in the churchyard, not the weathered burial chamber of the counts behind the wrought-iron gate, the crosses in amongst the ferns, the stone angels in half-relief above a crumbling bench no-one ever sat on, nor the plaque bearing the motto I did not understand, even that time when my mother read it out to me: "Love never fails." They were remnants of a past that, so it seemed, had been overcome once and for all.

It was an old, aristocratic family that had given the village its name, vassals of the counts of Gützkow and the dukes of Pomerania – "brave, beloved and trusty knights", according to an old deed of enfeoffment.

They are words from a fairytale. They appear in columns of dense writing in which the branches of the family trees go off in many directions. The von Behrs were squires and stewards, chamberlains and counts, provosts and professors, district and town councillors, curators and commanders, court tutors and cavalry captains, *valets de chambre* and young nobles in court service, soldiers, marshals, majors and captains, lieutenants – in the Polish war, in the Swedish household guard, in Danish or French service. A canoness and a prioress, a captain's wife, even a poetess. But most importantly they were the owners of this place, including their fief, their possessions, seeds, chattels and livestock. A feudal estate which, for lack of an heir, passed back to the old ancestral line in which, since time immemorial, the first-born had counted for more than those born later, and the daughters for virtually nothing. They had goods which they sold and exchanged, retained and acquired, collecting interest on them or pledging their shares in them. Sometimes they signed deeds of enfeoffment, affixed their seal to thick paper, a sticky mass, as red as ox blood: a dancing bear with a swan on either side.

My mother's ancestors were farmers, livestock and timber traders, carters and master butchers, a forester, a pointsman, a sailor. My father's ancestors, my biological father, that is, were millers and master tailors, cartwrights and carpenters, a musketeer, a few doctors, a seamstress of fine fabrics, a fisherman, a railway guard, a chemist, an architect, a factory owner, an armaments manufacturer, who after the war became a cemetery gardener.

We only lived in that village a year, but it is the first year I can remember. It was not the cemetery but the grounds of the mansion that our yard backed on to, my mother says. And there were also the remains of a tumbledown wall, she adds.

Some said the mansion was demolished after the end of the war, others that it had burned down before the end of the war, along with its entire inventory: the magnificent chandeliers in the entrance hall, the leaded glass of the doors to the two drawing rooms, the dark furniture, the books, the silverware and the china, the gilt mirrors, the old maps and the gallery of ancestors with its massive portraits of serious-looking gentlemen on large horses.

We do not own any old things, any heirlooms. Only the house we live in is old. At night you can hear the marten in the attic. My parents are waiting for a flat in the prefabricated building behind the swan lake. Three rooms, central heating and a bathroom with hot running water. They are on the waiting list. Time is short. The baby is due soon.

It was not uncommon for the old buildings to be in such a dilapidated state that they collapsed in the night, like the cooperative store the previous autumn. The roof had simply caved in. In the morning the door could only be opened with brute force.

I remember the cluster of people gathered in front of it, shop assistants and customers, women in flowery house dresses carrying limp string bags, men who came and pulled tin cans out of the rubble. They loaded the dusty goods into wheelbarrows and piled the tinned food, bags of flour and bottles that the milk float delivered in a dark, musty room on the ground floor of our building. An emergency sale got under way. The light was on all day. The ringing of the till could be heard all the way up to our flat.

I was wearing a sleeveless batiste sleepsuit with a pattern of tiny orange flowers on it. It had an elasticated waist. I remember the open window, the mild air, because it wasn't cool, it couldn't have been cool, and not so much as a breath of fresh air entered the room, for it was July, and Tante Kerstin's birthday, and why Tante Viola had not come to check on me I do not know. I was three-and-a-half years old, nearly four. Four fingers stuck up straight, nearly a whole hand.

I have no memory of a pile of bricks, of a heap of stones in the yard which, that day, I apparently climbed on, higher and higher, and kept jumping down from. I see only the open window. The windowsill is level with my chest. I try to hoist myself up, but it is too high. I take a few steps back, think: Judith, you are not stupid, and say: Judith, you are not stupid. I keep repeating these words, first quietly to myself, then out loud. The words lead me into the kitchen. I take hold of the kitchen chair and slide it across the tiled floor. It makes a loud scraping noise. I drag it over the threshold, I haul and heave it over the orange living-room carpet, over the threshold into the bedroom, past my parents' big bed to the window, which is standing open. I think of little Häwelmann in the fairytale, but my nightshirt is not a sail, nor is my cot on wheels. It stays put next to the heater all night. I peer through the bars. I stand at the rail. I am Häwelmann, but the moon, which, speaking in my mother's voice, asks "Surely that's enough?", has disappeared behind a cloud. Its edges glow. No-one can stop me. I clamber onto the chair, my feet in their slippers. Dark-blue corduroy ones. I climb onto the windowsill and crouch there. The toes of my slippers are pointing out into the open air. I don't wait. I don't wait for anything. I don't look at the lamp. I don't look at the branches of the apple trees. Only down. The pavement. The patch of greenery below me.

My mother leaves the hospital without a baby, takes the train to the new village, which has not only a bus stop but also a railway station. She walks past the church, on top of which there are storks feeding their young, past the co-op, a new building with bicycle racks on the concreted area in front. But the gossips in house dresses are already there. They look in her direction and whisper: a teacher from Behrenhoff who's just moved into the new block. They beckon her over and ask if the baby was stillborn. They ask in standard German and in dialect: Were 'e stillborn?

An old woman finds me. She leans on her walking stick, bends over me and says: A right pickle you've got yerself into, duck!

My mother comes home without a baby. She does not even come home, because while I am at my grandparents' for a week, my parents move to a new-build flat in a neighbouring village seven kilometres away, endlessly far away. Kilometres, that's the largest unit, as inconceivable as years. I am three and a half years old, nearly four, but this I only know because it is shortly before my fourth birthday that my brother has his first glimpse of daylight – or rather the strip lights in Greifswald women's hospital – and soon afterwards the light of the phototherapy lamp on his jaundiced skin. The flat has a bathroom but no central heating. In the cellar there is some coal left over from the previous tenants. It is enough.

Like a snake, the umbilical cord had twined itself around the baby's neck and first delayed his entry into this world, then complicated it and ultimately so jeopardised it that the live birth of the infant, whose hands and lips had already turned blue, bordered on miraculous.

I remember a nightmare in which I am underwater, sinking ever deeper, a layer of ice above me. I remember a cartoon on the television where a woman dives into an empty swimming pool and, like a doll, shatters into pieces. Even today that image still sparks a nameless terror in me.

I do not know what it feels like to be dead. I ask the teacher in my new kindergarten, a tall woman with a shock of curls.

She shakes her head. I don't know, she says. I've never been dead.

I want to know what happens to the dead and buried. They rot. I do not understand the word.

Like a wrinkly apple which, as time goes by, gets infested and eaten up by worms and maggots, she explains.

I find myself thinking of the rubbish bin in our kitchen, then she adds: You don't notice anything though. Because you're dead, of course.

Evil is the skin on heated-up milk, the thin layer of ice on the frozen village pond, the dozen shiny-black slugs in the yard. Death is an old woman in a flowery house dress. Goddesses of destiny wear a headscarf, walk with a stick and speak in dialect. They talk about stillborn babies, about a right pickle, and rake the graves of their prematurely deceased husbands.

The von Behrs were once brave, beloved and trusty knights. Their palace burned down, say some. It was demolished, say others. The villagers looted it themselves and set it alight when the Russians came and the old countess had fled, says one elderly lady, who ought to know. They took whatever could be taken: the magnificent chandeliers in the entrance hall, the leaded glass of the doors to the two drawing rooms, the dark furniture, the books, the silverware and the china, the gilt mirrors, the old maps and the gallery of ancestors with its massive portraits of serious-looking men on large horses, the silver cigarette case bearing the count's crest: a black bear rampant on a grey escutcheon, its front paws raised as if in greeting, surmounted by a helmet topped by two swans facing away from one another with curved necks.

I land in a patch of stinging nettles. My slippers still on my feet, an ache in my legs. A numb feeling. The stinging of the nettles. The silhouette of a hunched old woman in the light of the street lamp. The asphalt shines. It has rained.

I read recently that stinging nettles grow wherever people settle, by walls and among debris. Like most prickly and thorny plants, they have traditionally been ascribed antidemonic properties. Pliny writes that the root of the stinging nettle can cure three-day fever if, as you dig it up, you utter the name of the sufferer, and whose child they are.

I did not know whose child I was.

I see the dazzling bedroom light, the cupboard with its woodgrain pattern beneath its smooth varnished surface. I lie on my back with my legs in the air like a beetle. I see my parents, larger than life. They do not look at me, only at my legs, which they wrap in gauze bandages. My legs hurt, my feet are numb. Their faces are bright patches with hairdos.

Nothing was broken. The X-ray images left no doubt about it. Nobody spoke of a miracle. Neither my mother nor the doctor in the nearby town. The nurse wrapped my sprained ankle in a zinc-paste bandage. My vaccination card, which she stamped, had three strips of plaster stuck on the first page. On them were written in block capitals my name and my new address in the village by the railway line, in my mother's handwriting, a clearly legible teacher's hand.

Nothing was broken, but I was unable to walk properly for many weeks. I hopped and hobbled, I held my arms out. My mother picked me up. Legs wide, I cling to her hips, inside her belly the unborn child.

Later on, my parents often talked about all the troubles my leap had caused them. But not about happiness or about the miracle, because miracles did not happen at that time, in that country.

I knew no god and no angels. The first time I saw one, in a colourful framed painting above the curiously short bed of an old woman, I was already going to school. The picture was a relic from a bygone age as dark as all the rooms in the estate workers' houses with their rough stone gables and masonry, as remote as a world in which children are led away over a wooden bridge by the light of the moon by a long-haired man, colourfully attired, with large wings, glowing cheeks, blonde curls and shining eyes.

At supper I looked at my mother for a long time. Was she really my mother? Was it not possible that she was only pretending to have given birth to me, after days of pain, as she mentioned repeatedly? Was it not just as feasible that she had simply found me somewhere and kept me, or had taken me from my actual real mother, who was waiting for me somewhere, inconsolable, as in the song of Little Hans?

I watched her butter my bread, cut it into small pieces and put it on my board. I studied her brown eyes, her mouth that was hiding something. I ran into the bathroom and positioned myself between the two mirrors, stared at the image repeated ad infinitum and looked for similarities.

It was a riddle, but I did not even understand the question, the task before me. The question was an open window. The answer was an open window. A jump from a height of four metres.

Years later I am lying ill in bed at my grandparents'. It is the holidays. The guest room is unheated. I am in pain and running a fever. They call the doctor. A tall man, who lays his pale hand on my neck and studies me with a long, hard look. He has a soft voice. His eyes are so deep-set they look as though someone had pushed them back in their sockets, from where they now peer out all the more urgently, strangely enlarged by the glass of his spectacles. It is a look that is trying to tell me something. His hand slides a photograph out of his wallet. It shows a child with sturdy calves in white socks, a huge umbrella in her hand. I nod and am none the wiser. It is a riddle, but I do not even understand the question, the task before me. The child in the photograph is me. The doctor is my father, and is not my father.

More than thirty years later, one cold spring day, I hold a measuring stick up to the façade of the refurbished verger's house and am amazed that it is four metres exactly, to the last centimetre. The first-floor window has been widened. The old vicarage diagonally opposite is for sale. From its veranda you have an uninterrupted view of the open country, a flat landscape, meadows, fields with sandy, clayey topsoil. A man comes and points through the milky windowpanes. Saltpetre, he says. It sounds like a death sentence. Only now do I notice a white encrusted scum on the walls. It looks like an infectious disease.

For the first time I go into the church. On the north wall of the chancel is a painting of the jaws of hell. Frogs, snakes and people are tumbling in, condemned souls who are devoured by the flames. And sitting in splendour in front of all this is a pig-faced prince of hell complete with sceptre and lightning bolt.

Is the jump out of the window my earliest memory? I ask my mother about the hedgehog. The hedgehog appeared the year before, sometime in the autumn, says my mother. But I do remember the hedgehog, which has to mean that my earliest memory is of that curious creature, and not of that night in July.

The stone bears still stand supreme on their rendered pillars at the entrance to the grounds, their paws clutching the weathered escutcheons, the crest of the last counts. An avenue of lime trees leads into the grounds. The cobbles have almost sunk into the earth. A landscape full of rhododendrons, sweet chestnut trees and magnolias, with two copper beeches, even a red oak and a tulip tree. Spreading over the ground is a white carpet of flowering spring snowflakes, snowdrops and anemones.

At the edge of the sports field I discover the moss-covered stones of a hip-height wall. It must be the remains of the palace. It must be the remains of the mansion, which only became a palace when the only part of it left standing was the cellar vault. In the southern part of the grounds, a pair of swans sit in front of two artificial islands, as if painted.

Babylonia
THE SEVEN BOOKS OF MANI

* *Mani was born in the year 216 in Babylonia, near Seleucia-Ctesiphon on the banks of the Tigris, to Persian parents, and was raised by his father in a Jewish-Christian baptism sect on the lower Euphrates. From his earliest youth he received revelations. At the age of twenty-four he left the Elcesaite religious community and started preaching, gained followers and made enemies. He proselytised throughout Babylonia, in Media, Ganzak and Persia, in the land of the Indians and Parthians and on the fringes of the Roman Empire.*

Mani was patronised by the Sasanian ruler Shapur I and his son Hormizd I, before being imprisoned by their successor Bahram I at the behest of Zoroastrian priests in the year 276 or 277. He died on the twenty-sixth day of his incarceration. His corpse was mutilated and his severed head left to rot above the main gate of the city of Gundeshapur.

Manichaeism spread beyond Mesopotamia to the whole of the Mediterranean region including Spain and North Africa, as well as into Asia Minor and central Asia and along the Silk Road, reaching as far as the Indian and Chinese empires.

Its syncretic teachings incorporated elements of Zoroastrianism in Persia, Gnostic Christianity in the west and Buddhism in the east. In late antiquity, Manichaeism was a global religion with followers on three continents.

† *There are barely any sources describing the demise of Manichaeism, as practically all its writings were destroyed during ancient times and the Middle Ages, the practice of the faith was suppressed everywhere, and its followers persecuted. From the year 382 onwards, in the western Roman Empire, any avowal of Manichaeistic faith was punishable by death. In the Chinese*

Empire, the religion was not banned until 843, and it persisted in some parts of East Turkistan until the thirteenth century, and in South China even into the sixteenth century.

Although all Mani's books written in Eastern Aramaic once existed in translation in mission languages like Greek, Latin, Coptic, Arabic, Parthian, Middle Persian, Sogdian, Uygur and Chinese, virtually nothing has survived of these texts. All that remains is the beginning of the Living Gospel, *portions of the* Fundamental Epistle, *some fragments of the* Book of Giants *and a few snippets of the sacred book written in Middle Persian, the* Shabuhragan. *So for a long time efforts to piece together Mani's teachings were dependent on the testimonies of the persecutors and on Arab encyclopaedists of later times.*

It was not until 1902 that some poorly preserved fragments of original Manichaean manuscripts were recovered in the central Asian oasis of Turfan. Large parts of a Manichaean-Coptic library, found in 1929 near the Egyptian oasis of Faiyum, ended up in collections in Berlin and elsewhere. Some of these manuscripts which had not yet been analysed, including the volume containing Mani's letters, were lost yet again in the process of shipment to the Soviet Union after the Second World War.

And if holy things really are only revealed to holy people, then it would be here – in the shimmering noon glare of a high desert sun, beneath the ragged date palms lining the banks of a sinuous tributary of the mighty many-branching Euphrates, which in late spring swells with the snowmelt from the northern mountains into a torrential river prone to burst its banks and dams, pumps vast masses of water into the impressive channels of the finer and finer branching irrigation system, which reaches into remote, indeed the remotest rain-deprived and rainless lowlands, fills dyked basins, soaks fallow ground, makes bucket wheels turn and seeds sprout and flourish – and guarantees the two annual harvests that are the reason for this land's fame and riches: the corn, the mountains of pomegranates, figs and dates that float downstream on countless hundreds of rafts, until the water course, reaching the marshy delta, is united with its twin river and flows, swollen, towards the sea.

Here is the land of the beginning, the alluvial land of civilisation, to which our remote ancestor with his heavy skull and freed-up hands was once drawn, in the process driving his wide-jawed cousin with the nostril-like flared nasal orifices and the melancholy bulges above his primate's eyes ever further north, where he hid himself away in caves – armed with stone tools and bones gnawed bare – to die the unlamented death of his species. And out of the zigzag movements of the nomadic tribes there evolved a vague order: tribes became peoples who lined up their settlements along the meandering rivers like beads on a long, fine-spun thread, each town a kingdom in itself, a community of commoners who began to share the work and wages, the harvest, the yield – and, in the absence of stone, wood and ore, built themselves a world of clay: mortar-rendered reed huts and simple round buildings for the shoeless peasants, square palaces for curly-bearded kings, wind-buffeted citadels and dust-swept ziggurats, avenues of blue-glazed bricks guarded by bull-men and winged lions, gently raised reliefs of priests in long robes with crossed arms, densely inscribed clay tablets covered in dainty symbols like bird tracks in wet sand.

While those Adamitic tribes are still feeling the fleece of the wild sheep to test the woollen undercoat, snapping the ears of einkorn wheat off the stalks, collecting the husks of emmer wheat in brightly painted ceramic bowls and breaking up the earth with a crooked pickaxe prior to each new sowing, things, too, became more settled, supplies are accumulated and claimed as possessions, cattle are fenced in, wild horses tamed, land surveyed for the first time, and harvests eked out to supply the coming years.

Tribal community is followed by tribal economy. Honey flows. Souls wander. The stone age is drawing to a close. Bronze shimmers, iron gleams, the age turns first golden, then grey. And the more settled those peoples become, the more restless grows their quest, their desire for truth and meaning, an inner agitation which is as novel as the sight of the never-changing horizon that swallows up the sun each evening. They gaze into the darkness and see no land, only the flickering patterns on the insides of their eyelids and the bottomless blackness punctuated by glowing specks which engulfs anything that dares approach it. The world is day and night, heat and cold, hunger, thirst and repletion, a valiantly turning potter's wheel, a wooden cartwheel, the tip of a cane that works the wet clay as the ox ploughs the field.

In the beginning – only this much is certain – was work, the circling of the great *perpetuum mobile*, which, once in motion, preserves energy, causes the rivers to swell and flow into the sea and the water to rise up to the sky, feeds into the great cycle, the changing of the seasons, the return of the conceptual pairs that have been stepping up, two by two, since the dawn of history, to play heaven and earth, mother and father, brother and sister, a pair of deities, two monsters that hate each other's guts. The desolate emptiness of pre-history seems richer than the tedious law of opposites, which henceforward weighs like a curse on mankind, which from now on has to decide between gathering and hunting, ploughing the field and tending the flock, stoking the fire and going to the well. No-one can say what is awaiting understanding, there in the depths, at the very root of being. Whether, in the beginning, a storm of chaos reigned, or a gaping void, or both or neither, whether creation happened randomly or for a purpose, the result of a contest between different generations of gods, a battle between Old and Young.

The cosmologies that spring from here are as countless as they are contradictory. What unites them is the concept of the imperfection of this world. There is a rift, undeniably large, a painfully deep gulf between the gods and the people cast into this world, between the eternal, unblemished soul and corruptible and hence corrupted flesh. The questions, old though they may be, are more pressing than ever before: what man is, where he comes from, where he is going, when and why this world has heaped guilt upon itself.

For its guilt is proved by the drought that knows no end. The days when the seeds yielded a twenty- to thirty-fold crop and every spring rain transformed the steppe into a sea of flowers are past. Water accumulates in the flooded fields, the harvest is spoiled, while the unremitting current flushes more and more sand onto the southern bank of the river, and the sea gradually recedes, leaving behind nothing but scurfy marshland. Sometimes rain falls, sometimes not. When the water levels rise, even just a cubit higher than usual, the floodwaters arrive too early, inundate the lowland, wash away the dykes and destroy the harvest, then the currents breed nothing but hunger and agony – and the memory of that great flood, on whose fatal waves a pitch-sealed wooden box carrying a select few drifted towards a new era, an age in which one of the gods conquered the others and, like a king, issued laws: no alliance without conditions, no trust without a contract.

And yet the moods of that god are as fickle as the currents of this river, and as contradictory as the auguries of the seers who read the future in the twitching of lambs' livers and the twinkling of the stars. For here, on this sweeping plain with its draughty steppes and fertile river valleys where the pictures once crystallised into writing, everything is full of signs that need deciphering and interpreting. They are tidings of fate, messages from the sky, that truly endless sky above the steppe, from which a voice

now begins to speak: call it spirit, call it wind or breath! When
an angel speaks, one must listen. And so, in a palm grove on the
lower Euphrates, a child, barely any older than the boy Jesus
among the temple elders, cranes his neck and hears what the voice
has to tell him: "You are the apostle of the light, the last prophet,
the successor to Seth, Noah, Enos, Enoch, Sem, Abraham, Zoroaster, Buddha, Jesus, Paul and Elkesai — and the one who will
complete all their teachings." The revelation is like a boast. This
angel is bragging. And what is the child doing? He is afraid and
requests proof. So the angel does what angels do. He comforts
the boy, sends signs and miracles, makes palm trees speak in the
manner of men and vegetables cry like infants, and reveals to him
one of those secrets which had hitherto been hidden from the
world: that the fundamental drama of the universe was a battle
between light and darkness, and this existence nothing but a
transition between two eras.

Whoever wants to will understand. And the boy Mani wants
to. He wants to take up the place assigned to him, to become the
glorious culmination — to be the last in a line of great prophets.
But since no-one ever believed a child, he has to wait. What does
a Chosen One do, whose time has not yet come? He prepares
himself. He studies the teachings handed down from his predecessors. Great men, all of them, ascetics, prophets, semi-deities.
They had all accomplished much, yet must have failed, since he
was now appointed to finish their works.

Anyone can practise asceticism, renounce the world and resist
the devil. Many have heard God's word and more than a few
have proclaimed it. Yet even those angelic tidings are blown away
by the wind. Who is supposed to gather them up and one day
proclaim their wisdom if time disperses them? Words become
verbiage, and a vision becomes a mirage. That which shall become
truth must be written down, says the angel. That which shall

remain truth must be written down, thinks Mani. Only the written word will be proved right and will endure, will weigh as heavy as the material on which it is captured, a chunk of black basalt, a terracotta tablet, the flattened fibres of the papyrus plant or the stiff leaf of a palm.

Years pass. Understanding forges a path for itself, a veil is lifted, content reaches for form, craftsmanship for art, the verbal for the written. A remarkably clear shape crystallises in Mani's mind, a circle, as round as a compass-drawing, as complete as his teachings, which reconcile the beginning with the end, cyclical thinking with linear.

Autumn is already well advanced when Mani's time finally comes. The Euphrates lies there as ever in its winter bed, a feeble rivulet trickling along a groove in the wide, sandy river bed, making it easy to forget that it was its water that once supplied the seven terraces of the Hanging Gardens with the aid of endlessly rotating screw pumps.

And Mani sets off in a northerly direction, towards the town of his birth on the left bank of the Tigris, passes through the gate guarded by winged creatures of stone, mingles with the crowds streaming by, raises his voice and speaks the words that prophets have spoken since time immemorial: "You are the salt of the earth. The light of the world. He who follows me shall not walk in darkness, but shall have the light of life."

People stop. The reason is unclear. Perhaps it is the heat that prompts them to seek a moment's rest, or the strangely lopsided figure of Mani, so appealing and yet repellent that, even in passing, one cannot help noticing him and his stunted leg. But perhaps it is also his message, in the light of which all colours disappear and everything turns black or white: the soul good yet lost, the material world evil and corrupt – and man a ligature combining both, who yearns for salvation and purification. It is a

contrast that creates clarity and promises purity, that darkens the
world such as it is and at the same time presents the bright prospect of a remote but safe future which claims to be nothing other
than the recreation of a lost, perfect prehistoric age. It is the
good news in a country full of good news, the gospel at a time
of gospels aplenty, the answer to many questions. Mani can read
these questions in the faces, now, as the sun reaches its zenith
and siesta time approaches. And since he knows that in this land,
you are only heard if you are able to talk about the beginning, he
starts to relate how everything began: in the beginning, before
the world came into being, everything was good. A wind blew,
gentle and fragrant, light radiated in every colour, peace and con-
tentment reigned. And the god who ruled over that realm was an
eternal god, a good god, the father of greatness, the lord of light.
For an eternity, peace prevailed in this paradise, and nobody was
bothered by the smaller, tumultuous land of darkness in the
south, where the princes of the individual provinces had waged
war on each other for as long as anyone could remember. Indeed,
the two powers lived side by side; the light shone for itself, the
darkness raged against itself; the one fulfilled its own purpose,
and the other likewise. Until one day – no-one can say when
exactly – the darkness attacked the light and both were drawn
into the battle, the soul versus the material world, unlike versus
unlike, and the second, middle era began, the great universal
drama, the Today, Here and Now in which mankind is trapped.

Mani speaks the softly undulating Aramaic of the east, but
his words are incisive and brook no contradiction: everything
in this world, he repeats, is an amalgamation of good and bad,
of light and darkness, of soul and matter, of two natures that are
intrinsically separate, as life is from death. Therefore one must
not feel at home in this world, nor even build a house, and must
neither conceive children nor consume meat nor yield to carnal

desire. All activity should be limited to what is strictly necessary, to keep contact with the material world to a minimum. For the ploughing of the earth, the cutting of vegetables, the picking of fruit, yes even the crushing of a blade of grass underfoot damages the sparks of light they contain.

He pauses and listens to the effect of his words. A good speaker knows when to stop talking.

And so, before long, he withdraws to one of those caves in the semi-desert that are the dwelling-place of prophets, sits down on his left leg and puts his right leg, which refuses to obey him when walking and which he has had to drag behind him since he was little, out in front of him as a prop. On it he places a codex, unties the strings, opens the book, touches the reed pen to the blank sheet and begins to write on the unlined page – a few lines of that immaculate script that he invented: it is dainty and delicate, and even a thousand years later what is left of it, though barely visible to the naked eye, will be razor-sharp and legible under the magnifying glass.

Mani turns the page, he applies the brush to the papyrus, he paints the teeming creatures of darkness and the creation of the world: the way the Lord of Light peels the skins off the slain demons and uses them to line the firmament, the way he forms the mountains from their fragile bones, the earth from their limp flesh, and the sun and moon from the sparks of light released in the battle, and he also paints the divine messenger who set this cosmos in motion and each heavenly body on its orbit. And then Mani turns over a new page and sketches the panorama of a disturbing truth: it was the Lord of Darkness who created the first human couple, modelled on the image of the divine messenger, from the pitiful remnants of the light – and implanted in them the deplorable urge to conjoin and multiply. The first human beings cling tightly to one another, two naked pale figures who conceive child after child, thereby dispersing the light into ever tinier particles and pushing the day of their homecoming to the kingdom of heaven ever further into the future.

Mani cuts the gold leaf into minute pieces, sticks them to the papyrus and keeps on applying opaque pigment until the page shines brightly. Morning comes. Evening comes. Days and weeks go by. Mani does not cease painting: the vast revolving, never-flagging wheel of the cosmos which little by little drives all light from the world, the virtuously waxing and waning moon – a golden ceramic bowl in a night sky of lustrous lapis lazuli – in which the light is collected and cleansed of any traces of earthly grime before returning home on brightly shimmering ferries via the Milky Way, having escaped the cycle of birth, a light-bearing soul that is allowed to cease existing.

Finally, he reaches for the squirrel-hair brush and goes over the folds of the messenger's robe one more time, the eyebrows of the Mother of Life, the contours of the gold-gleaming armour of Primeval Man, the goaty grimaces of the demons. Even the beard-hair of the Lord of Darkness and the claws of his scaly feet he paints with the diligence of an artist who loves all his variously shaped creatures equally and even forgets that evil was never good, was neither related to good nor its offspring, was not some fallen angel or rogue Titan, and that there was no accounting for its wickedness. In Mani's miniature it is a self-savaging monster with a dragon's body, a lion's head, an eagle's wings and a whale's tail, which since the dawn of time has been ravaging its own kingdom – a battlefield obscured by clouds of ashes, poisoned by the foul stench of carrion, full of dead tree stumps and seething scarlet abysses with chrome-yellow smoke rising out of their depths. Mani's doctrines may be black and white, but his books dazzle with colour. Whoever possesses such books has no need of temples or churches. They are themselves places of contemplation, of wisdom, of worship: magnificent codices, the weighty tomes bound in unsplit leather, the counterspaces delicately inlaid with thin slivers of tortoiseshell and ivory, in convenient duodecimo format, their covers clad in gold leaf and trimmed with precious stones, but also books as tiny as a charm that can be hidden within a closed fist. The ink made from pomegranate and lamp-black has a uniform raven sheen to it on the chalk-whitened papyrus, on pale silk, soft leather or gleaming parchment. Only the titles are decorated to the point of illegibility, twined around with flamboyant floral rosettes and edged with dots of crimson, the colour of redemption and destruction, the colour of the world-conflagration. Scarlet glows the fire which has blazed for one thousand four hundred and sixty-eight years, which has set the cosmos alight and will not cease burning until its heat has freed the last particle of light and consumed the entire universe. And the glorious images of the future shine brightly, a heavenly world of light in opaque white and gold leaf, in which good and evil are separated again, all parts of the darkness submerged, conquered and engulfed, a lump buried alive, and all parts of the light raised up, purified in the moon, cleansed by the rotation of the stars. Whoever wants to may believe it. Many want to.

Zoroaster had numerous pupils, Buddha five companions, Jesus twelve disciples – but Mani had seven books which carry his teachings out into the world in many tongues, uniting what was split apart by the building of the Tower, and dividing like no man before him: into those who follow him and those who curse him. They call him Mana, vessel of good or vessel of evil, and they call him Manna, bread of heaven or opium of villains; they call him Mani, the winged saviour, or Manes, the monster with the lame leg, Mani, the enlightened one, who set out to redeem the world, or Manie, the insane one, who set out to corrupt that same world – Mani, the balm, Mani, the plague.

And as the time of his martyrdom draws near, Mani speaks to his people: "Heed my books! And write down the words of wisdom I have spoken from time to time so that they are not lost to you."

They are ablaze. Pure gold flows from the fire that devours them. Yet it is not a world conflagration, not a flaming cosmos that consumes the sacred writings of the Manichaeans, but the pyres of their enemies. No objection is tolerated, and every doubt punished. For with the believers come the godless, with the pious come the heretics, and with any true teaching comes the swiftly inflamed zeal of those true believers who separate right from wrong as strictly as Mani separated light from darkness. The fire is not choosy, even though they say that the flames consume only what is untrue.

What else burns along with the holy scripts of the Manichaeans? Calculations of the end of the world and innumerable books of magic, evocations of the devil and countless conflicting philosophies of being, thousands of copies of the Talmud, the collected works of Ovid, treatises on the Holy Trinity and the mortality of the soul, on the infinitude of space and the true magnitude of the universe, on the shape of the Earth and its position in the configuration of the stars. The interrogations last for days, the pyres burn for centuries. The fire warms the hearts of the omniscient, it heats the baths of Alexandria, Constantinople and Rome, until the eye can no longer deceive the mind, and books start to be informed by nature. How immense does the truth have to be for its light to outshine the darkness of all the errors surrounding it? Every time a new telescope is invented which brings the far-off ominously close, the boundary has to be moved, horizons enlarged: celestial spheres turn into orbits, circles into ellipses, patches of fog into globular clusters, spiral nebulas and galaxies, six planets into seven, eight, nine – and then eight again, and mysteries into forms of matter whose genesis is no less eccentric than Mani's cosmology – suns that maintain planets on their orbits, black holes that rend and swallow up stars, fogs that radiate light that in the distant future will be received by no-one. No matter how many numbers and formulae describe the cosmos, no matter what knowledge illuminates its nature: as long as time still exists – and who could doubt it? – then every explanation remains no more than storytelling, the familiar tale of attraction and repulsion, of beginning and ending, of coming into being and passing away, of chance and necessity. The universe is growing, expanding, forcing the galaxies apart; it is almost as if it were fleeing from the theories that attempt to capture it. And the notion of this flight, of this rampant growth into the anchorless void seems more terrible than that of a shrinking, a contraction back to the ancient raw point where it all began, where all power and mass, all time and all space fused, coalesced, a dot at first, then a lump, buried alive: an explosion, a dilating space, a hot, pressurised state, expanding, cooling, until atoms are formed, light and matter separate and create the visible world – as improbable as that may be: suns, clouds of molecules, dust, cosmic worms. Asking about the beginning is asking about the end. Whether everything will expand and accelerate, or will one day go into reverse and contract back into itself, caught up in loops that know neither birth nor decay. After all, what do we know! Only this much is as good as certain: there will be an end to the world, possibly a temporary one, but still the most appalling thing imaginable: the sun will swell to gigantic proportions, swallowing up Mercury and Venus, and the whole of Earth's sky will be nothing but sun. And its immense heat will evaporate all the water of the oceans, melt the rock, rupture the Earth's crust, turn its insides out, until cold descends, the end of time.

But for now the sun hangs large as a ball in the glorious deep-blue sky above a land with a history going back many millennia, one that considers itself as old as humanity itself and knows only a pair of opposites: the murderous desert of sand or stone and the life-giving water of the River Nile, which, every summer, used to flood its valley for a hundred days, transform its alluvial land into a huge lake and leave behind it that greasy, earthy-black sludge that rendered the soil so fertile. But since its floodwaters have been dammed up behind massive walls and forced into a labyrinth of thousands upon thousands of channels contained by dykes and dams and levelled out by weirs to provide year-round irrigation for the fields that are expanding ever further into the desert and wring two harvests out of even the sandiest soil, the beneficial Nile flooding no longer occurs. And the ancient Fellahin people native to the area, who since ancient times have worked the earth with strong-boned oxen and wooden ploughs, have no choice now but to send the children into the desert, to the rubbish tips of abandoned settlements, to hunt for sebakh, the nitrogen-rich fertiliser produced by the decomposition of the sun-baked mud bricks that formed the walls of ancient towns.

It is a particularly hot day in 1929 when three teenagers roaming around the sanded-up, semi-submerged ruins not far from Medinet Madi discover in a vault a rotten wooden box that, on exposure to sunlight, immediately falls apart revealing a number of disintegrating bundles of papyri. Water has permeated the sheets to the extent that, despite having resisted countless generations of worms and populations of ants, they have been eaten away not by living creatures but by the finest salt crystals, so that the men who, not long after, hold the codices in their hands in the room of an antique dealer initially hesitate to pay good money for these black-edged, stuck-together book blocks. Even the restorer who eventually examines one of the musty packages doubts whether its age-old secrets can ever be coaxed out of it.

Only after months of work does he succeed, with the aid of an inclined plane and tiny tweezers, in unsticking individual sheets, which are so wafer-thin and fragile that a sneeze would be enough to reduce them immediately to dust. Call it chance or destiny! While in Berlin manuscript experts hunch with their mirrors and magnifying glasses over the silky-sheened remnants of an evidently sacred scripture pressed flat under panes of glass, in a Californian observatory on a mountaintop not far from Los Angeles, the physicist Fritz Zwicky points a 200-inch reflecting telescope at an area of sky within the Coma Berenices constellation. And as he observes the movements of the blurry fog patches, which reveal themselves to be separate galaxies, and compares them with his calculations, he is hit by a realisation.

Never could visible matter be sufficient to hold these clusters of galaxies together. There must be invisible matter in the universe whose presence is indicated only by the gravity it exerts. It was this that began to coalesce a fraction earlier than other matter, its gravity laying a trail that everything else had to follow. A mysterious force, a new celestial power, which Zwicky, on account of its unknown nature, names "dark matter".

Meanwhile the manuscript experts in Berlin have arranged the scraps under the protective glass in order and are starting to decipher the skilful writing. The fragments prophesy the downfall of Mani's community, and describe the atrocities committed against its members. But they also proclaim:

A thousand books will be preserved. They will come into the hands of the just and the faithful: the *Gospel* and the *Treasury of Life*, the *Pragmateia* and the *Book of Mysteries*, the *Book of Giants* and the *Epistles*, the *Psalms* and the *Prayers* of my Lord, his *Icon* and his *Revelations*, his *Parables* and his *Mysteries* – not one will be lost.

How many will be lost? How many will be destroyed? A thousand lost, another thousand recovered; for they will find them at the end. They will kiss them and say: "O Wisdom of Greatness! O Armour of the Apostle of Light! When you were lost, where did they find you? I rejoice that the book came into their hand." And you shall find them reading them aloud, uttering the name of each book among them, the name of its lord; and the name of those who gave all for it to be written and the name of the scribe who wrote it and of the one who punctuated it.

Rycktal
GREIFSWALD HARBOUR

* Between 1810 and 1820, Caspar David Friedrich painted the harbour of his native city of Greifswald crowded with the masts of sailing ships, among them galleasses, brigantines and yachts. The old Hanseatic city was connected with all the major commercial centres via the navigable estuary of the river Ryck, which flows into the Baltic Sea, and even though the channel of the river Ryck was much broader then, it frequently threatened to silt up.

† The 94-centimetre-high, 74-centimetre-wide oil painting had been in the possession of the Hamburger Kunsthalle since 1909, and in 1931 went on show at Munich's Glass Palace as part of the exhibition Works by German Romantics from Caspar David Friedrich to Moritz von Schwind. *On June 6 a fire broke out there that destroyed more than three thousand paintings, including all the works in the special exhibition.*

The problem is not locating the source but making it out. I am standing by a meadow with a map in my hand which is no help to me. In front of me is a ditch, the water not deep, the channel at most half a metre wide, the water's surface covered with a holey carpet of yellowish-green duckweed. Sedge grows along the bank, yellow and pale as straw. The place where the water apparently rises to the surface from the depths of the earth has been colonised by thick green moss. What did I expect? A bubbling spring? An information board? I refer to the map once more, look for the slack blue line that starts in the eggshell-coloured open terrain below the green-shaded woodland area. It may well be that the true source is more likely to be found up there, in the forest stretching out behind the handful of houses which turn this spot into an actual place with a name that I was able to tell the taxi driver. No doubt he was wondering what I was planning to do here, especially on an Easter Saturday, but in this part of the country, curiosity alone has never tempted anyone into speaking. The people here are serious and indifferent – as if submerged in a nameless sorrow – and, like this landscape, get by perfectly well without words.

This wholly inconspicuous rivulet probably is, in fact, what I am looking for: the source of the Ryck, formerly the river Hilda, which supplies the port of Greifswald many kilometres seawards of here, before flowing, broad and almost majestic, into an inlet of the bay, the Danish Wieck. I see the fissured, greying timber of the fence posts to my left, the two lines of rusty barbed wire, behind them the grassland dotted with countless mounds of freshly dug earth, the work of industrious moles, and, as was my intention, start to follow the upper course of the river in a south-westerly direction.

The great blanket of cloud spread out across the sky hangs low and heavy over me. Only in the distance are there breaks in the cloud, giving a glimpse of a streak of pale powder pink. A few broad-shouldered oak trees stand overlooking the paddock, remnants of a wood pasture long since cleared. Their branches are reflected in the hollows brimming with rain and meltwater, big as lakes. Grass grows up like rushes out of the pale-blue pools. A wagtail runs through the water, dips its tail feathers in a curtsey, and takes off on its springy flight.

Encrusted patches of March snow, barely three days old, glisten from the shaded grassy corners, from the indented tractor tracks, and from the white plastic wrappings covering the round bales, in which the hay ferments into silage. An overturned trough is rusting on the riverbank. Spreading above it are bare branches of hawthorn, its bark enveloped in sulphur-yellow lichen. The trumpet call of the crane rings out, triumphal and indignant. Beyond the ditch, two lead-grey birds raise their oversized wings and propel themselves into the air, only to wheel around ready to land again not long afterwards – in perfect unison, their legs reaching out towards the ground – and with three breathless beats of their wings come to a standstill. Their call resonates for a while longer, until it is finally swallowed by the east wind. It hisses in from the sea, a piercing wind that sweeps moth-grey oak leaves before it. The arable soil feels soapy underfoot. Blackish brown lumps of clay lie bare and sodden on the surface. In the furrows, rape is sprouting, its leaf edges already stained peroxide blonde by pesticides. The colours are pale, the light feeble, as if dusk might descend at any moment.

In the lee of a swampy depression, a herd of deer browses. As I draw closer, they gallop down to the wood, their white flags flashing. On the edge of the kettle hole a scrap of camouflage material flutters on the frame of a raised hide. Not far off some mossy concrete roof slabs are piled up in front of leafless hedges of bramble, elder and blackthorn. Rusty loops of low-grade steel poke out of the reinforcement holes, now exposed and at the mercy of the weather. Moss as black as algae has taken over the porous blocks. Behind this, sheltered by the sparse undergrowth, a streaky green pond lies quietly in its ice-age hole, a spawning place for frogs and toads which wait, out of sight, for the signal to procreate. The withered grass has dried to a waxy yellow, bleached by the winter. Only the leaves of the buttercup burst in abundance, spinach-green, from the damp black earth.

I go back to the ditch, follow it until the water disappears underground in a concrete pipe. On the horizon, the bright blades of the wind turbines go round, living machines. I think of the black horsehead pumps I saw as a child, and their sinister stoical thrusting into the depths of the earth. It was the last ice age that formed this region, the lowlands of the Ryck valley, a tongue-shaped basin in a gently undulating moraine landscape, its fields and kettle holes edged with massive boulders worn smooth by sandy debris and glacial water. The deeper layers hold rich resources of crude oil and salt.

A few hundred metres further south-west, grey-barked birches mark out the onward path of the stream. I cut across country until I reach its now slightly broader bed. The narrow unploughed strip meanders between the field and the ditch, barely two metres wide. The carpet of greenery is ripped open in places. The peaty earth shimmers damply, churned up by wild boar. A skylark ascends, warbling, into the sky and its breathless song announces the spring, though it seems far-off, inconceivable even. For the first time the water is audible now too. It flows, gurgling softly, towards a patch of woodland and disappears beneath some hazel bushes. I plunge into the intimate stillness of the wood. Here, sheltered from the penetrating east wind, the ground is still thick with the withered, ash-coloured fallen leaves from the previous year. The undergrowth is earthy and grey, all except for the heath pearlwort, green as parsley. And the winter aconites on the point of blossoming into egg-yolk yellow stand erect with their leaves fanned out. As the wood begins to thin, I discover – among brushwood, pine cones, and deer scat with its blue-black sheen – the shed antlers of a stag. The dark brown bony structure weighs heavy. I run my hand over the pleasantly chapped, leathery hard surface with its knobbly protrusions, and over the smooth tips of the tines. At the bulging ring that was once attached to the pedicle on the stag's skull there are still tufts of hair from the ani-mal, which must have discarded its headgear only recently. The alabaster-white, scabbily rough bone tissue at the rupture point feels sharp as coral. It must have taken some strength to cast off the antlers. The bark of the nearby spruces is streaked with score marks. Milky resin hangs from the wounds like frozen blood. Some trunks have been gnawed bare by the hungry deer.

A gust of wind rustles the treetops, the sky brightens, and for a moment the pale disc of the sun glows through the wall of cloud. It casts no shadows, but immediately there is a buzz of activity in the air, and the birds grow louder: the mechanical chatter of the magpies, the unflagging song of the chaffinches, the tuneful warble of the blackbirds and the melancholy sing-song of the robins.

As I emerge from the wood, a carrion crow takes flight, sails, cawing, over the field speckled green with winter barley, swoops down time and again without interrupting its hoarse call. The landscape looks different, peaceful, tidy. A perfectly straight clay footpath lined with leafless willows follows the ditch as far as the next hamlet. Schnapps bottles from obsolete brands lie in the water. Arching out left of the footpath from the withered undergrowth are reddish-grey bramble stems. Birds' nests are perched in the bare hedges. And beneath a hawthorn bush lie dozens of chalky-pale, shattered snails' shells and the stones where blackbirds and thrushes have smashed the armour-plating to extract the soft flesh. The mud churned up by tractor tyres and softened by rain and meltwater yields underfoot with every step I take. The puddles have taken on the colour of their surroundings. It is the umber of wet clay and the murky swamp, a uniform waxy hue with little in the way of contrast, save for the spring-green tinged branches of pussy willow quivering with silvery young catkins in the frosty air. Their silky fur has only just unpeeled itself from the sticky buds.

At the edge of the city the watercourse forks. I follow the most inconspicuous of its branches, the stream hidden deep in the scruffy field margin and lined with crack willow. The trees rise up out of the karstic brushwood like bulky beings moored upside-down to the undercut riverbank, their crowns pollarded, their branches stunted, hollowed out by wind and weather. Rotting wood bulges from their burst insides.

Soon the footpath crosses a water channel which, on the map, now bears the name of the river of my quest. Uncurving, it heads east, breaks loose from its surroundings, a natural boundary between two paddocks, hemmed in by willow fences. Lying on the meagre soil of the riverbank are blades of sedge beaten flat by the rain. Silently the water follows the course designed for it, fed by more and more drainage ditches branching off to the north and south. The open countryside lies there frigid. Everything is remote, the land occupied, cultivated, providing pasture for cattle still crowded in their sheds. Only the wind rages, whipping my breath away, stormily impeding my steps. The sky is clustered with bulging clouds. The hum of traffic is audible from somewhere near or far.

It is a while before anything catches the eye again. Dogwood and blackthorn bushes enclose the fields and provide shelter from the harsh north-easterly. A flock of greyish-brown, blackbird-sized birds swoops over the fields, repeatedly touching down en masse to rest, and taking to the air again at the slightest disturbance. They are fieldfares, the grey-speckled thrushes that feature in the cookbooks of bygone days, which overwinter in the Mediterranean. Yellowhammers, too, soon appear as dabs of broom-yellow in the gusty air. Imperceptibly the ditch grows fuller, the water level rises, the channel broadens out, the rippling water flowing through the open shutter of a mechanical weir.

When, after a time, a road approaches and crosses the ditch, the smooth, tin-grey asphalt is alien to me. Cars zoom past. To the north, shiny concrete-grey barns, bilious-green silos and a greyish-white pyramid of plastic-wrapped bales of straw are visible through a row of poplars. From somewhere comes the drone of farm machinery. Solitary flakes of snow dance noiselessly above the boggy ground of the yellowed pastureland.

In the grass of the riverbank I find a brown-grained river mussel, as large as a chicken's egg. Its inner surface shimmers in shades of mother-of-pearl. Not far off, some mallard ducks are dabbling in the water. They fly away with an irritable whining and flapping as I approach, more easily startled than their town-dwelling cousins, and gather on the nearby fallow field. Their webbed feet show up in shades of orange and the heads of the drakes shimmer peacock-blue against the grey expanse of the field. After the monochromy of the last few hours, the birds' bright colouring appears almost exotic.

Then I arrive at the place I had picked as the end point of my first leg. The little village of Wüst Eldena consists of not much more than a restored manor house and a row of brick-brown farmworkers' cottages. Apart from a dilapidated fire station and a few tumbledown barns, all the buildings look lived in: there are curtains hanging in the windows, cars standing on the driveways, and chickens strutting along by the fence surrounding their run. Neglect pervades the place. Its name is an empty claim. It refers to the Cistercian monastery at the mouth of the Ryck, Greifswald's ancient founding building, which has been languishing in a state of ruin since the Thirty Years' War.

My mobile phone has reception again. I dial the number, and just as the taxi appears at the end of the lane, snow begins to fall steadily from the sky in big thick flakes.

Three weeks later, the world is divided into a *Not Any More*, an *Already*, and a *Not Yet*. It is the end of April. Everywhere else spring is well advanced. From the train I saw green-stippled hedges and the white blossom of the blackthorn bushes. But here in the far

north-east the lingering chill is still delaying the appearance of
the new spring shoots. The sun is shining, but with a pallid light.
It has no warmth as yet. As always, the four-lobed flower-heads
of forsythia are the first to appear, though it is not yet a blaze
of sulphurous yellow. A milky haze lies over the village, which,
with its gardens and sheds, soon gives way, beyond a hedge of
fast-growing poplars, to pale-green pastureland. The rigidity is
unlocked, the frozen ground thawed, the land peaceful, innocent,
almost shy. Crack willows and birches still stand bare, though
the outlines of their branches are enveloped in a soft bloom. The
briar hedges are only just coming into leaf. Blackthorn leaves are
unfurling in yellowish rosettes. A few withered berries from last
summer still hang in the branches. Their gentle shade is home to
creeping ivy and delicate, pale-downy stinging nettles. A young
chestnut tree displays its crinkly leaves freshly emerged from
their glossy buds. The farm track, two gravelled sandy ruts carved
in the turf by cars and farm vehicles, hugs the line of the ditch.
In the hedges of dogwood and blackthorn, sparrows fluff up their
plumage. Blackbirds chirp, a blackcap warbles, and a chaffinch
recites his never-changing tune. At some point the fences have
all vanished. Broken reeds surrounded by the remains of rotting
leaves poke up out of the flat water that lies virtually unclouded
in its rusty-brown bed. And the layers of rushes felled by the
autumn winds, when they were dry and brittle, glow like straw on
the pale-green grass of the bank.

Feathery cirrus clouds veil the upper skies, criss-crossed by
dissolving aircraft vapour trails. Grey-green woods border the
eastern horizon. To the south, the countryside unravels into scattered settlements, individual trees and kettle holes. To the north,
clouds of dust billow in the wake of a ploughing tractor. A bluish
cereal crop is emerging out of the ground in the nearby field.
The smell of slurry pervades the air.

The field margin is awash with the chrome-yellow of lesser celandines, dandelions and marsh marigolds with their waxy, heart-shaped leaves. A small tawny-coloured tortoiseshell butterfly flutters past. A bumblebee buzzes in search of food. Dead-nettles stand tall on their lofty stems, their purple-lipped petals protruding beyond the stamens.

To the left, beyond some weather-beaten pine trees and a bank of mossy boulders, a copse stands entrenched on a slight elevation. Sprouting in front of this is a colony of brown spore-bearing spikes resembling the capped stems of black morels. It is young horsetail, a vestige of ancient times, the farmer's enemy. And flourishing in the middle of the footpath is a crop of tiny marsh gentian in all its pale violet glory. High in the sky, which is now clear, kites circle, rise and fall, bank and swoop daringly on the lookout for prey. The landscape is tinged by an ash-blonde light. The earth seems to breathe in long gentle breaths. Below the mirrored surface of the water, many-stranded pondweed sways with the soundless current. All at once a heron takes off from the water, rising into the air on outstretched slate-grey fans, water droplets fizzing from its wings. It labours skywards in a wide arc and flies seawards, its head flat and tucked in. Then Sunday quiet is restored. The path mimics the bends of the ditch, the water flowing at a leisurely pace along its imperceptible descent. At one point the water is dammed up in the reservoir of a pumping station. Motionless, the sinister greenish brew stagnates beneath a scum of semi-rotten reeds and duckweed in front of the low-ered wooden sluices. Signs warn that it is forbidden to swim or to enter the enclosure. A narrow iron bridge leads across to the other bank of the clear waterway, now broad as a river, where, beyond open fields and embankments flecked with linden-green, further patches of woodland come into view.

A common toad sits in the sap-green grass. The tiny thumb of

its right hand is resting on a stalk. Beneath heavy, half-closed
lids its copper-red eyes stare at nothing in particular, the only
movement the pulsating of its wrinkled, agate-brown body. It is
covered with warts and grains of sand.

People appear as if out of nowhere. A boy speeds across the
clearing on a quad bike. A spaniel follows him, barking. A group
of adults walk by with a young child in tow and disappear behind
the pumping station without a word of greeting. I stand still and
try to locate the confused landscape on the map. The air is fresh
and clear, and for a moment I even imagine I can taste spring.
The map shows neither a riverside path nor any entry point into
the forest. All the marked footpaths start out from the inside of
the wood.

I want to follow the watercourse into the willow marsh, but
after a bend in the ditch I come upon a festering black bog. The
squelching sodden soil impedes my every step. The ground grows
ever softer, and I sink ever deeper in the miry, bare earth. Water
holes of fathomless black shimmer from the bottom of the
hollow. I realise that I can go no further this way and must turn
back. So I pick my way through the pale-green dappled woods of
the water meadow, bending young branches aside with my arms
until, some way further south, the ground, now concealed by
undergrowth, hardens. From beneath the faded carpet of leaves,
light-craving anemones raise their heads, showing as flecks of
white on the cool forest floor. A woodpecker raps a tattoo in
the treetops. Filtered light falls on the slender shoots of hazel, the
young beeches and slim birches. Before long tall spruces cast
deep shade on the ground, which is springy now, and strewn with
scaly pine cones and yellowed needles, then, as I pass under oaks
and beeches, it grows lighter again.

There are signs everywhere of animal activity: the reddish loose
detritus churned up by wild boar, the dark entrance to a fox's earth

or badger sett under a root, the hieroglyphic drawings of bark beetle larvae on a bare stick, and the high-pitched voice of the bullfinch. Several times I reply to its cheerful single-syllable call. And when I lie down on the soft grass of a small knoll in the dappled semi-shade of some pine trees, the bird ventures out from his cover and perches in the boughs directly above me. Its breast is a radiant vermilion. I answer it again, and so we go on, taking turns for a while, until all of a sudden it launches into a rousing, completely different tune in five verses, which I am unable to imitate.

I close my eyes, and the tangle of branches reappears, imprinted on the blazing red of my eyelids. The shrill cries of birds of prey can be heard in the distance.

When I set off again, the sun is high in the sky, and its light, for a moment entirely undimmed in the dusty clearing, gives a foretaste of the shimmering, scorched sand-flavoured heat of the summer, the sound of the sea. From time to time, the rhythmic loop of the bullfinch's song rings out again. I amble through plantations of young and more mature trees. The ghostly shadows of the kites circle over the washed-out sandy soil, which glistens with the burst, honey-scented pods from which hornbeam leaves have unfurled.

I re-emerge into the open, and a hare darts out from the young rye only a few metres from me, doubles back on the farm track and disappears into a tilled field. To the east, a flock of rooks passes above some drooping power cables, cawing hoarsely. A stork sails over them with outstretched wings to its nest overlooking the gables of all the houses in a nearby village, and in the shady margin of the wood another ditch peters out, bordered by an ash-coloured belt of strawy sludge. It must have been washed up by floodwater, along with the succulent finger-leaved yellow irises, and masses of pale-violet molluscs, which resemble fossils on the dried mud.

The Ryck itself runs further to the north. I want to take a short cut, so I clamber under electric fences and cut across country, directly through grazing land. But soon every step I take is hindered by the wet, and wherever I tread, the waterlogged ground yields beneath my feet. Further north, the Ryck is eventually joined by the abundant waters of the river Riene, before flowing, contained by slightly concave dykes, towards a village. A prefabricated high-rise is already visible from far off. When I finally reach the riverbank, the first seagull appears in the sky without a sound, black-headed, ready for the breeding season. For a moment the air tastes salty. The village street leads across a level bridge. A siren wails. And above the wooded horizon, the deep-blue sky is turning a misty white.

When I cross this same bridge three weeks later, the riverbank is lined with knee-high grass. The sky is leaden. Heavy, bulging clouds cast a gloom over the land, all except for the western seam of the horizon, behind me, which glows with a streak of ivory light.

I follow the watercourse eastwards past tousled clumps of withered reeds. A Haflinger mare and her foal graze in a lush green paddock. Warblers babble from hedgerows newly in leaf behind drifts of gangling stinging nettles. From a farm building comes the whine of a chainsaw. Its rising and falling din accompanies me for a long while along the small dyke streaked lavender-grey with vernal grass, and mingles with the call of the cuckoo, clear as a bell, from the green-tinged white willows on the south bank. When I return its echo-like call, it hisses like a cat and flies from tree to tree in search of its rival. Above it, in the higher reaches, three grey herons drift solemnly, with angled, unmoving wings towards the bay. House martins zigzag busily back and forth over the rippled surface of the water, on which the occasional lily pad floats. Lupins hold their pale-blue flower spikes majestically aloft. Herbaceous speedwell with its little bluish-violet flowers and the tiny feathery shoots of yarrow appear dainty and fragile by contrast. Rotting amongst the fibrous broadleaf plantain is the scaly-blue gleaming rear end of a half-eaten perch, which must have been left behind by an osprey. Lanky bittercress dots the hay meadows birch-white. Caramel-breasted whinchats flit, chirping, from stalk to stalk. From the quivering reeds comes the vehement call of the reed warbler, followed soon after by the melodious piping of the golden oriole from a nearby wood.

I try in vain to locate it. Instead, way out to the east, I spot a black and white creature rising up out of the water and spreading its board-like wings wide. The sheer size of it alone makes it seem strange, almost unearthly. I stop walking and take up my binoculars. An osprey? No, it must actually be a sea eagle, which has now found itself a lookout point some distance away, ready for the next stage of its hunt. Not far from it, beyond fields of buttercups, the oilseed rape is a blaze of brilliant yellow. Standing tall again in the distance are the wind turbines with their grey propellers. All but one are motionless. Further eastwards, a crop sprayer makes its way across a field of barley, sprinkling as it goes.

Because all this is happening on the other side of the river, it seems far away, as does the group of people, even though we are separated only by the river channel. They stand, arms folded, next to a tractor with a large water tank. A St Bernard pads around, brushing past their legs, examines the submerged red pipe, walks to the small blue-and-white painted pumping station and barks across. Are they collecting water? Or pouring something into the Ryck? For decades, newly dug ditches have been draining ground water from the marshes to transform the poor grassland into arable land. Indeed, I soon stumble across an offshoot which disappears into the thorny scrubland bordering an adjacent wood.

Bubbly black mud oozes in the undergrowth. Tired light filters
through the tree canopy. Silence reigns now; there is not a bird
to be heard. It is not long, though, before I am back in bright
light again, because a swathe of the wood has been chopped down
to make way for overhead power lines. Japanese knotweed has
run riot here, growing several metres tall, with large oval leaves
and flailing bamboo-like canes. I walk on and take the first turning leading out into the open.

On the edge of the wood, a profusion of hawthorn flowers
forms a luxuriant froth abuzz with insects – while the middle of
the white clover-dotted meadow is home to swallow-wort and
western marsh orchids with purple, helmet-like flower spikes and
broad leaves marked with reddish-brown spots. And for a moment
Greifswald cathedral and directly in front of it the brick-red
pyramid of the tower of St Jacobi's appear between the riverside
copse and a far-off embankment.

A barely distinguishable path leads alongside the waterway,
now framed by dykes on both sides. Behind the strawy palisades,
graceful, clean-limbed birch trees stand tall, their fresh leaves
fluttering like bunting. Swaying in front of these are the frayed
pennants of the reeds. Yellowhammers repeat their uninflected
tune, a chaffinch chip-chips. Soon another, smaller pumping
station comes into view on the far bank, its façade daubed with
graffiti. An angler casts out her fishing line in front of it. Two
large brown dogs are lying next to her. Soon afterwards, in the
middle of my path, I come across a thick bronze-coloured bone
sticking up out of the dried earth of a molehill. It appears to be
a cow's femur. A thicket of eared willow is lush with bristly
yellowy-green flower spikes. The Ryck, entirely overgrown with
buckthorn and reeds, is no longer visible. The reeds rustle. Azure
damselflies flit among the branches or sit on stalks of meadow-
grass, the hint of a horseshoe mark on their iridescent abdomens.

A sound now reaches my ears that I cannot place, a dull metallic clicking, which is repeated soon afterwards. And then, behind a bank, the freshly mown green of a golf course opens up before me, its artificial hillocks continuing right up to the bypass embankment. People in brightly coloured peaked caps hit balls into the air, while from the dense hedgerow next to me a thrush-nightingale pipes up, more strident than a nightingale but just as brilliant.

The hedges that hemmed me in a moment ago have given way to a carpet of butterbur. Snails have munched holes in its rhubarb-sized leaves. A trail leads through a boggy willow grove and under the road bridge, then up again to a pedestrian bridge. I rest my hands on the parapet and look at the peaceful, brownish, roughly three- or four-metre-wide watercourse, which only officially counts as the Ryck from this point, the outer limit of the city. Lily pads float at its edges.

All at once the sky clears, and I feel the sun burning my neck. I take the sandy farm track along the top of the small dyke on the south bank. I pass a meadow of buttercups, before coming upon the municipal cemetery. On the far bank is a row of detached houses. This group of dwellings is not shown on the map. It must have been built only recently. In the branches of a hawthorn bush choked with knotweed glows a spot of rusty red. It is a common linnet, and a hand's breadth away from him, larger and less colourful, is the female. But before I can get a closer look at them, they both swoop down and disappear. Soon the Ryck is hidden by the reeds again, and only the blue railway bridge in the distance reveals which way it flows from here.

My path takes me further south past a fire-fighting pond ringed by barbed wire and pink-blossomed apple trees. The trunk of a willow has been colonised by ochre-yellow slime mould. It looks like construction foam. Tall poplars line a cracked asphalt road leading into town. Horses graze in a paddock, and soon after, beyond a small stream, are some blocks of flats. There are plastic slides and trampolines in the gardens. On the other side of the street is a huge derelict storage depot behind a holey wire fence. Soon I reach Grimmer Strasse with its narrow, pastel-coloured old buildings. I walk past a farmyard and across a super-market car park. In a paved yard in front of a stonemason's premises, two Rottweilers growl behind high fences. They have rubber chewing rings in their mouths, drool hanging from their chops. The Ryck is a long way off. It is only when, walking along the earth rampart, I turn into the park surrounding the zoo that am I able to spot its reed-fringed bed again behind a disused rail-way line. I follow the pavement downhill, past the old hospital building where I was born. After the bridge on Stralsunder Strasse, the river opens out and flows into a trapezoidal basin some seventy or eighty metres wide and several hundred metres long – Greifswald harbour. Two floating restaurants are moored to the paved northern quay, and several tall-masted sailing boats to the southern quay. Behind them, the prefabricated buildings cast long shadows.

I sit down on the south bank. On the other side is a line of low buildings and wooden sheds, boatyards and a rowing club where, as a youngster, I trained one spring. Somewhere behind it, in the Rosental valley between the Ryck and the Baberow, is where the saltpans must have been which – together with the river – were the reason why woodland was cleared here and a market town established on swampy ground. A dead bream floats in the brackish water. Swifts dart low over the rippled surface with shrill cries. Three swallows are perched on the taffrail of a schooner, their fox-red breasts aglow in the evening sun.

la psychopathologie d. l. vie quotidienne
Gehirn und Seele
la science des rêves
Psycho-synthese
das Unterbewusstsein
Einführung in die Psychologie
hypnose, suggestion
Ecole Nancy
die Selbstbemeisterung durch bewusste Autosuggestion
die Desuggestion
William Harvey 1578–1657 découvre la circulation du sang
Wahrheit und Schönheit
Psycho-analysis

Valle Onsernone
ENCYCLOPAEDIA IN THE WOOD

* *At the age of fifty, Armand Schulthess, a clerical assistant in the commercial section of the Swiss Federal Department of Economics in Bern, decided to start a new life from scratch in Ticino. Schulthess, who in his younger days had run a ladieswear company,* Maison Schulthess, *with branches in Geneva and Zurich, gave up his office job in 1951 and moved to Valle Onsernone, having already purchased several plots of land there, eighteen hectares in total, in the 1940s. From that point on, his life revolved around a grove of chestnut trees, which he gradually transformed into an encyclopaedia in the wood, organising human knowledge by subject area and inscribing it on more than a thousand metal plates. The often multilingual inscriptions included summary descriptions of different fields of knowledge, lists, tables and bibliographic information as well as suggested leisure activities, interspersed with invitations to get in touch, though any actual attempts were always emphatically rebuffed. Schulthess lived the rest of his life in seclusion. He died on the night of September 29, 1972 in his garden from exhaustion and hypothermia following a fall.*

† *In July 1973, his legal heirs had his house cleared, which had been crammed from wall to wall with books, papers and household items, and burned or disposed of virtually its entire contents. During the clear-out, which took two days, a library of around seventy hand-made, probably collage books on the theme of sexuality was incinerated. The outdoor collection was completely destroyed. Only a handful of the metal plates and nine of the hand-made books were salvaged; three of these books ended up in the Collection de l'Art Brut in Lausanne, while the rest are now in private ownership. Today the house's name is the only reminder of its former owner:* Casa Armando.

Testing, testing, one, two, three, four, five. You're listening to Radio Monte Carlo. Testing, testing, six, seven, eight, nine. Good. Let's get going with our evening programme. So, we have now arrived in the village in the Onsernone valley. The village is about two hours from Locarno. You take the train and get off in Auressio. It's a bit of a walk to the house. You take the little footpath downhill. You'll come in May as the weather's nice then. You'll find the house easily enough, and the sign outside that invites you to knock on the door as the bell isn't working anymore. You'll encounter Gorgo at the front door and brave her stare. You'll see the garden, all the metal plates. You'll read them, understand them. It's a large site, a nice piece of land: sloping, rocky, covered in dense chestnut woods. It falls away steeply towards the south. From the fence at the bottom you can hear the burble of the river Isorno. The old main road runs right through the site. Nowadays it's a public footpath, so I have strangers walking across my plot of land, domain number one. I also own domain number two in Alp Campo to the south of the mountain pass into the Maggia valley, and domain number three in Sotto Cratolo.

The people who come here read the plates, but they don't read properly. They don't know how to read; they only read to stimulate their minds, to stimulate their feelings. But you have to read to organise. And whatever's being organised has to be written down first. That's the only way to create order. My system is based on putting like with like: the "Miraculous" section groups the phenomena associated with the cult of St Thérèse of Lisieux and the tears of blood and stigmata of Therese Neumann of Konnersreuth together with the astonishing invulnerability of Mirin Dajo, who allowed his body to be pierced with swords, and, right next to it, the world's greatest maritime disasters. The Nobel prizes go with the encyclopaedias, Linné with the plants and animals, the butterflies with philosophy, fertiliser with a diet table, radiesthesia and radiation with gambling odds, the moon landing with U.F.O.s, U.F.O.s and fakirs with parapsychology and the mysteries of mankind. The table of sunspots with the barbecue, the secrets of Tibet right behind the psychoanalysis tree and the plate about ant colonies directly above the anthill. The written word must connect with the real-life experience. An encyclopaedia in the wood. Human knowledge is assembled here. It hangs in the trees. It is not complete, of course. It cannot possibly be complete. What a job that was, writing all those plates! You must always do something useful in life. Collect something if you're out and about, pick up an apple, a chestnut, a tin can. Everything has a use. You mustn't throw anything away, not even a scrap of paper. You can do accurate work even with pencil stubs. Tin cans can be turned into signs, if you flatten them out. There is always work to be done: weeds to be got rid of, rusty signs to be repaired, chestnuts to be peeled. They swell right up and take on the taste of whatever you put them in. In syrup they turn really sweet. And in a broth they become savoury. They have a high nutritional value. It is important to know the nutritional value. Especially when you don't have any teeth left. I can't eat almonds anymore. I'm a good cook. For lunch all I need is a pint of milk and a bread roll. There's nothing one really needs. One doesn't need anything really. At most a woman. She should be interested, keen to learn, young. Someone who knows nothing yet. Someone I could teach about everything. Ideally a young girl between eighteen and twenty-five who I could marry or adopt, an orphan or a young heiress.

You won't break things, unlike the children who sometimes visit, who don't answer when you speak to them. Not even when you ask what language they speak. I speak German, French, Italian, Dutch and English. But the people who come here only want to collect chestnuts and make fun of me. They haven't got a clue. Take no notice of them. He's a weirdo, they say, a nutcase, a lunatic. Just because I sometimes play the gramophone at night. The fact is, the acoustics are best in the open air and at night-time. It doesn't disturb the birds as they're asleep. Sometimes I like to sing. As long as no-one hears. I used to sleepwalk as a child. But then I grew out of it. Enrico Caruso was the greatest tenor of all time. I've got a lot of records by him, and a hundred and fifty records in total: operas, operettas, classical music, dance hits, the most famous of the Viennese waltzes. It's all there. You love music.

There are plenty of lovely places to sit and relax all over the site. Above the cold buffet there's a water feature, a little gully made using the traditional drystone wall method. Two grottos that supply the site with water all year round, an open-air cinema, a fire pit and a bathing spot. I went to great trouble to set it all up. I layered hundreds of stones on top of each other, dragged tree trunks and branches uphill to make it a nice place, a place of beauty. Because beauty is important. Everything – life, progress – depends on beauty. Those who make light of beauty don't realise how much our lives depend on it. When I met my first wife, I was wearing a coat from Paris, a beautiful piece. That's why she married me. She was already pregnant at that point. Misshapen by the bulge on her front. First the money dried up, then so did our relationship. We had a child. But before long it was dead.

The niche in the wall there might make a nice little spot in the summer. There are still some fireclay plates in decent condition on the rubbish heap. I'd just need to bring them over here, and they'd make a good cooking spot in the culinary arts department. You'll learn how to barbecue food. There's a griddle pan with a lid you can use. Or you can wrap the food in tin foil to cook it. At a Mexican barbecue they actually roast a whole animal that way. There's a large library of books on a culinary theme, including the popular titles *Second Only to Love* and *What Men Like to Eat*, lots of barbecue recipes and marinades, as well as books on cultivating an allotment or kitchen garden and a volume on the language of flowers in French. When you come, it'll be summer. You'll enjoy the cool shade. You'll hold on to the old iron bars, climb down the rock face on the little ladder, balance across the narrow bridge over the ravine and arrive at Casa Virginie, a single-room building with a flat roof and no terrace, measuring four metres by four. I built it myself, a year before I embarked on my second life, my actual life, the dream of self-sufficiency. That was in 1950. You can see the plans for it on a board at the house. If you live like me, it's free. I don't rent it out. You have to earn the right to stay there. It's called The Cottage or else Casa Virginie, after the state in the Wild West, after a female person, after a physiological state. That's also why the front door is bricked up. There's a bell at Casa Virginie that rings through to the bedroom in the main house. Everything's there: nice wallpaper, nice curtains, a lampshade, even benches to sit on, and brackets for window boxes of geraniums. You can live in it if the separate little room gets too small for you. It'll only take a night to unbrick the door. By the light of the moon is best. It's light enough then. And nearby you've got the big windmill I designed myself, along with its generator, and the components for the water pump, which is nearly ready. Power generation is a problem in itself when you want to be self-sufficient. Chickens would be good. They lay eggs. They're very useful. It would be easy enough to build a henhouse out of windscreens. The chickens need a ladder, a hierarchy, a system. The whole plot is on sloping ground. So the gradient's already there. I had goats once. But they were stupid. I put down a mattress for them in Casa Virginie, got them settled on it for the night and even covered them with blankets. But they kept getting up again and went and slept on the floor. Three or four goats, it was. Later I tied them to the trees with a rope. They went round and round and kept on walking in circles until they got all tangled up. Then one day they were dead. They were nice animals, a nice breed, sadly just very stupid.

If you carry on along the footpath, you'll arrive back at the house and see the big celestial disc on the east gable showing all the constellations of the zodiac. The skies interest me, human destinies, blind chance and the connection between all things, the mechanics of life-threatening events, events that cause premature death. You'd really need to collect specific case histories with dates of birth and dates of ill fate, analyse them and work out rules from them. The more cases you studied, the more accurate the results. You'd need to write up the horoscopes for certain days: the day Swedenborg was born, the day of the break-in at the house of Erich Maria Remarque, the day the pop singer Alexandra died in a car accident. About twenty cases of people dying out of the blue like that. You're bound to find something in common. But, alas, almost nobody knows their exact time of birth. Goethe said: As the clock struck twelve, I came into the world. That gives you something to work with, at least. The timing of one's birth isn't random. Not many of those born on the same day as Mussolini survived. You see, every day of one's life corresponds to a year of one's life, and if a crisis occurs in early infancy, which is indicated if the planets Mars, Saturn, Uranus and Pluto are positioned at zero, ninety and one hundred and eighty degrees to one another, it is repeated in the corresponding year of one's life and signals death. You can find all the calculations for this in the astrological folders at the house. And there are plenty of examples available of skies associated with birth deformities. My calculations are precise. The biological recurrences form an obvious pattern: certain events occur on these nodes, giving rise to

highs and lows. Longevity and length of life are age-old preoccu-
pations. But everyone has to die. That's a fact. That's a comfort.

The best thing in school was giving a talk. You could pick a
topic and find out everything about it. Because it's important to
know what's what, to be well informed, whether from a historical,
geographic or fashion perspective. You can deliberate over the
way things are and will be. One school of philosophy after another
has done just that, and each of them has come to some conclusion. In the East, you reap what you sow. That's what is meant by
karma. You'll find plenty about that in the books of theosophy.
Questions concerning the soul are all addressed in the theology
books. Our impulses, perceptions, inhibitions, memories and so
on are dealt with in the psychology books. You see, the Ego, the
innermost core of our being, shouldn't necessarily be regarded as
merely a reflection of our body. You can find out more about that
in the books of anthroposophy. A lot stays in our subconscious.
It can cause inhibitions and neuroses. Psychoanalysis brings it
out into the open and provides release. Infants' perceptions are
still completely undifferentiated. Then, very slowly, they become
polarised. Sigmund Freud discovered that many of the errors we
make stem from the repression of our sexual drive. Someone else
demonstrated how the desire for superiority is all-determining.
And individual psychology is the result. Professor Jung is the one
who discovered the archetypes – the universal, inborn patterns
that reside in our collective unconscious. Coué of the Nancy
School demonstrated the power of suggestion. Parapsychology
examines phenomena that cannot be explained by our everyday
senses, while astrology collects past evidence and considers
whether the celestial configuration on the day of one's birth has
a bearing on what follows. Darwin demonstrated the evolution
of and relationship between all living beings, whereas Genesis
describes how the spirit breathed life into matter. Some say

spiritual beings exist on as yet inhospitable planets. The problem with spiritualists' professed contacts with the dead is that nothing positive ever emerges. One mustn't forget, though, that the fourth dimension is outside of space and time. Perhaps everything really will grind to a halt. There are still quite a few unanswered questions: the problem of divining rods, of death rays, and of whether Eusepia Palladino's séances were a matter of pure trickery or only occasional trickery.

I used to arrange everything very precisely by field. Physics here, bones there and parapsychology over there. Today, though, it's all a big mess. Knowledge proliferates. The trees just get bigger, they spread out, they reach up towards the sky until the writing peels, the wires come undone and the plates drop off. At first I used to repair them, but then it happened to more and more of them. It's not possible to work in the wood when it's dark or raining. That just leaves the house. It's old and, like most houses in Ticino, has granite walls. It has a stone roof and a lot of rooms, just no heating. You don't really need it anyway. In winter you can cover the floor with cork tiles, newspapers and linoleum and insulate the walls with jute and battens. Plastic bottles work too. When it's cold, you can put them in sacks and use them as a quilt. The Valvoline engine oil canisters work best. Those should never be thrown away. But people are forever throwing stuff away without a second thought. Especially the visitors. The rubbish heaps are real treasure troves. The things that end up there! Dolls, magazines, stilettos. There's a use for all of it. Once there was a radio lying there which still worked. In the evenings, after work, I listen to Radio Monte Carlo between 9 p.m. and 2.30 a.m. We'll be able to listen together. There's not just one radio, but three, as well as three bathtubs, two boilers, two refrigerators, seven electric mixers, but one doesn't need anything really, not even a toilet. One doesn't even need other people. At most a wife. A dog would be good. I've got a dog harness, and a brochure on breeding dogs.

Sometimes the front door won't open. It's because of the folding grille, which often gets jammed, and all the chestnuts blocking the entrance. There are newspapers, slips of paper and photographs everywhere. I always used to copy out the newspaper articles and file them in their correct place. Now there are so many of them I no longer even find time to read them. But I make lists of keywords, which I keep. For later, when I happen to have time, or in case people come looking for something.

My guiding principles are: read everything that can be read. Put like with like, and keep everything you've read. Only write down facts, knowledge that can be verified. Wherever possible, keep phenomena separate from established rules and always start with the general and work towards the individual. Because what's on the outside always points to what's on the inside. You can deduce more about my essence from my room than from my lung or my heart. That's because the external and the internal go together, just as the external sexual organs of the man and the internal ones of the woman are two variants of the same thing. And just as the garden is my domain, so the house will become yours. You'll see that sometimes the interior and exterior are out of balance. But in summer the shade of the chestnut trees and the findings of science can help with the heat, while in winter philosophy can help with the cold. Sometimes in winter I have to go outdoors to warm myself in the snow. A hot-water bottle can be a lifesaver. If you put it on the stove it saves you having to add hot water. I used to have a flat, curved metal water bottle to put by my feet. Nowadays I use a proper bottle and hold it to the sensitive place between my legs, as that's the best way to get the heat circulating.

There is a lot of equipment. Each item is inventoried: AS1,

AS2, AS3 and so on. I have the AS6, the film projector, the AS2, a video camera – a massive drum duplicator, a Rajah photographic enlarger, a beaded screen that makes the projection appear brighter and more lustrous, a reducer that allows you to make images so small they fit on a tiny bead, a low-frequency amplifier, a Thorens wax-disc cutter, the AS7, as well as books describing the physical processes involved in engraving your own 33 or 78-r.p.m. gramophone records. I used the AS7 to record a serenade by Enrico Toselli on the clarinet, which I'm going to play you by way of welcome. Now, too, the buttons are pressed, the stylus is cutting, the turntable is turning constantly, recording everything I say. The microphone is older. For very short-distance experiments there is also a mini-transmitter and a short-wave adapter, plus a crank telephone and a device used to produce stereo images. I wanted to try it out once. But the female just ran away. You really have to keep an eye on women.

I have the *Encyclopaedia Britannica*. I have numerous books about problems to do with love and marriage. I have books on the problems of existence and books about death. If you copy out keywords that interest you from your Brockhaus encyclopaedia and bring them with you, then I can copy out the same ones for you from my *Encyclopédie Larousse*. They complement each other, you see. The largest flower is the corpse lily from the Philippines, the largest den that of the grizzly bear, and the largest bird is unable to fly. Milk stays in one's stomach for two to three hours. The navel divides the human body roughly according to the golden ratio. One's arm span is roughly the same as one's body length. All living tissue is made of carbon compounds. The male is an accident: the female would have sufficed, writes Gourmont. She always has the principal role. This is evident if only from the fact that, in civilised humanity, more females are born the closer civilisation comes to a state of plenitude. The egg, recent research has shown, is by no means passive: it actively sends out a crude extension in the direction of the approaching sperm cell. Something grows on the ovary, something resembling a wart. When it bursts and drops off you get a rise in body temperature. It's called ovulation. And that's when you need to take care! I once had a girlfriend in Paris; she was from Mexico. And we had sexual intercourse. One time Aunt Flo didn't come. So we went to the pharmacy and the pharmacist gave her something to take, I think it was called Algos. And then the blood came, and in amongst all the blood was a tiny something. I've never seen anything like it. On holiday in the Tyrol I once had intercourse with the chambermaid. But I was still afraid after the last time. So we drove straight to Innsbruck to see a doctor, to check if anything had happened. But he just laughed.

The first on the right is my bedroom. It's always dark in there. The lightbulbs have blown, and the window is insulated with books. Only in the morning does a little bit of light filter through the gaps. It's like an alarm clock, a reminder to get up. And there are the women gazing out from the Lux soap advertisement and the magazines. They look straight at you. You can walk around the room, but they're everywhere, looking at you. Never averting their gaze. One of them is hanging on a coat hanger looking out from the top of a jacket. I dressed her in it. But her face is still naked. So much skin. Even when I'm lying in bed she sees me, looks down on me from above. Watches everything I do. Sometimes lust gets the better of one. Then one needs to find an outlet, especially if one's sex drive is very strong. Apart from masturbatory release, there are only three forms of sexual activity, the context and acceptability of which depend on the prevailing social climate at the time: there is prostitution; there is the free bond of love; and there is the officially governed and recognised contractual sexual relationship of civil marriage based on Article 4 of the Civil Code, section 1, paragraph 1353. In biological terms all three involve the same thing. I've been married twice. Both marriages ended in divorce. We weren't a good fit. Not even in the place where we should have fitted. Plenty of people have written about it. It's in all the books. There is, says La Rochefoucauld, only one kind of love, but there are a thousand imitations. One has to question one's own inclinations. Do they stem from an inner urge, or from the lure of the forbidden? Perverse sexual inclinations mostly develop at an age when the sex drive has not yet erupted. The person may well have a certain innate predisposition, but in the vast majority of cases, these preferences develop when one is experiencing the heights of ecstasy for the first time. The actor can portray nothing that is not already latent within him in some albeit rudimentary form: king, beggar, patriarch. As for the urge to dress up, there is a distinction to be drawn between transvestites, who like new clothes that don't come with memories attached, and fetishists, who like clothing that carries the hint of another person, in other words who love worn items.

You know what's cruel? Rousing a man into a passion with kisses, with all kinds of exposures and disclosures, touches, looks, by the way you read to him, talk to him, unreservedly inflaming his desire, but then, contrary to all the promises made, not being willing to go all the way – apparently solely in order to heighten his agony and allow you to revel in the sight of this suffering.

There is no denying the superiority of female beauty. Its source, its secret lies entirely in the unity of the female figure. What makes the woman more beautiful is that her genitalia are out of sight. The male sexual organ, which offers no advantage whatsoever except when it comes to answering the call of nature, is a constant burden and badge of shame. Our upright posture, especially, makes it the most vulnerable place in combat and an eyesore to behold since it is a bump in a flat surface, a blip in a smooth line.

The harmony of the female form is far more complete, if only in terms of geometry, particularly if you think of man and woman in the heat of desire, at the moment when they are engaging in the most intense, most natural manifestation of life there is. The woman, whose stirrings all occur internally and are expressed only in the undulating motions of her body, preserves her full aesthetic value, whereas the man sinks, as it were, to the lowest animal-like state, appears humiliated, forfeits all beauty the moment he exposes his genitals. In terms of technical ability to achieve coitus, too, the woman is superior to the man since she does not, for example, need an erect member to accomplish the act. As far as the mechanical process is concerned, a woman is capable of uninterrupted intercourse.

The size of the clitoris can vary greatly. However, a relatively undeveloped clitoris can, as indeed can the entire genital apparatus, grow in size over the years if the woman engages in plenty of sexual activity. No-one has yet studied the effects of practice and experience. In most cases, the larger labia are close together in women who have not given birth. They need to become engorged and the clitoris must start to become erect prior to any act if the woman is not to be left unsatisfied. Most married women submit passively to sexual activities and thereby miss out on the chance to ease and enhance the experience by getting involved themselves and controlling the relevant muscles.

You take the ladder to the first floor. You climb up it, rung by rung. It's still dark, but you'll be able to feel with your hands that you're going the right way. There's a ring dangling from the ceiling. You can grab hold of it in an emergency, if you're in danger. After all, there's not a lot of space up there. And there's even less as you go on. But you'll fit through. At the back you've got the balcony with two sun-loungers, though the balcony door is blocked up with books. Books make an excellent insulating material, you know. Not many people know that. There's a lot that people don't know. Then it'll get a little lighter, because on the left is your space, your domain, the separate little room. Sometimes the door won't open. And you'll be coming in autumn. Everywhere will be full of sweet chestnuts. The whole valley, the garden, the house. They fall down. They fall on you. They could strike you dead. The largest of the three fruits tastes the best. The nuts are glossy, their shells prickly. The tip of the nut is hairy, a sweet down. Like burrs, the chestnuts collect everywhere. The only clear space is in the separate little room. The chestnuts don't get in there. They don't belong there. Because that space is yours. Everything is there, close to hand, in the place where it belongs: the window behind the books, the dressing table next to the mirror, on the window ledge a little washbasin, a watering can, a fire pump, and the little hollow among the piles of paper, that's it — the sleeping space I've made especially for you, the female. Everything is ready: the mattress on its wooden frame, a nice bed, the fabulous clothes and furs. All of them the latest fashion. You can try them on. Hanging on a coat hanger is a yellow-and-green-patterned ladies' swimming costume. The other coat hangers are spare. You can hang your own clothes on them.

You'll look around, see the two nude photographs above the bed, and right opposite them the black and white nude photo of a young woman lolling on a sheet, the romantic images of couples kissing, the classical relief of a pair of lovers. You will look at your reflection in the mirror on the dressing table, and find everything you need there: nail varnish, beauty magazines and brochures, books on hat fashions and hair care, along with the book *Female Attractiveness and Beauty. What a Girl Needs to Know*, studies on pregnancy, fertilisation and the menopause, menstruation pills, an ashtray, a pair of scissors, a powder compact, toilet paper. Everything is catered for. An alarm clock, lots of hot-water bottles, a washbasin and water jug, a radio and a vibrating device.

Once some girls turned up and walked along the winding footpath. Unfortunately they were stupid, though they could read. Not that that means anything. Nowadays everyone can read. They were two sisters. Or so they told me. They came into the garden. They read and looked and were even pretty. Young, at any rate. They said they were hitchhiking. Not many cars stop here though. After all, the valley doesn't go much further. It doesn't lead anywhere. Only into the grotto. It's nice there. Damp even in summer. I nearly thought one of them was you. I showed them the house. They laughed when they saw the newspapers and the chestnuts. And again when I showed them their sleeping place and when I gave them ravioli from a tin. They kept laughing. Even though that's a perfectly decent meal. Yet when I knocked on their door they just screamed and ran away. I was only going to tuck them in. Tuck myself in with them. Show them everything, teach them everything. I was glad when they were gone. They ate too much anyway. The stupid nanny-goats.

There's an illustration in the book about the female organs of sexual arousal containing a view of the vulva. It shows the external pubic area of a deflowered woman, those instruments of the sublime orchestra that has so many different names, and is symbolised by the peach or the seashell. You can see the mound of Venus and the pubic arch, the large and small labia, the urethral, anal and vaginal openings, the perineum, the vestibular glands, the vestibular bulbs and the hymen. The pubis is a well. It is damp, fathomless and smells of moths and moss. A precise opening, a hollow, an abyss, a blind chasm. Desire is boundless and hard to pin down. There are so many questions. The term psychosexual perversion should be used with care. Every abnormality is rooted in the normal. And every normal state contains a grain of abnormality. Every pervert retains a tiny remnant of normal perception.

How do you define perverse, anyway? A man actually looks much more elegant in women's stockings than in socks and suspenders. The sexual practices of male and female homosexuals are no different from those of people of normal sexual orientation.

There is a remarkable photograph in the book *Abnormal Traits*. It's obscene. It's beautiful. You won't want to look at it. You won't be able to take your eyes off it. An emotionally charged scene: first you see a man and a woman, the woman's buttocks, the act of coitus. But then you'll notice that they're both wearing black silk stockings, and realise that the phallus is not a real member, but is fastened around the woman's buttocks with two transparent straps, the kind that are popular these days. Like must go with like. It's the only way to achieve order. A friend sent me the photograph a long time ago. Nowadays I no longer open any post. I haven't known anyone for years, so that's that. The postman used to come once a week to check if I was still alive. Now he doesn't come anymore. I don't open letters either. After all, you never know what they might say. It might be you writing to say that you don't want to come anymore. How am I meant to reply to that? Anyway, at some point I would work out for myself that you weren't coming. I couldn't send you anything either. And who knows whether the postage stamp I have is still valid? Who knows whether the letter would arrive? Who knows whether you would read it? So it's better to keep it. To keep everything. There's nothing one really needs. Just a pint of milk, a bread roll and a radio that plays through the night.

East Germany
PALACE OF THE REPUBLIC

* *Designed by a collective of architects led by Heinz Graffunder at the East German Building Academy, the symbolic government building was erected on the derelict land known as Marx-Engels-Platz on the former site of Berlin's City Palace, which had been demolished in 1950. It took thirty-two months to construct, and was inaugurated on April 23, 1976 as the People's Palace.*

*The most conspicuous feature of the elongated, five-storey, flat-roofed edifice was its façade of bronze-mirrored windows framed by white marble. The building housed not only the plenary chamber of the East German parlia-*ment or Volkskammer, *an auditorium accommodating nearly eight hundred and another holding up to five thousand people, but also several conference and meeting rooms, thirteen restaurants, eight bowling lanes, a theatre and a discotheque.*

It was the social hub of the party and state leadership, the home of the party conferences of the Socialist Unity Party (S.E.D.) and the seat of the Volkskammer, *a venue for major national and international conferences as well as a cultural and entertainment centre. The "Glass Flower" in the forty-metre-wide, eighty-metre-long double-height main foyer was a popular meeting place. Its walls displayed a collection of sixteen large-format pictures by well-known East German artists entitled "May communists dream?"*

† *To enable the building to withstand the pressure of the groundwater in the glacial valley of Berlin, a concrete slab one hundred and eighty metres long, eighty-six metres wide and eleven metres deep was cast as the foundation. A skeleton of steel girders was constructed around eight concrete cores, before*

being encased in asbestos cement. A special legal provision permitted the use
of sprayed asbestos, even though this technique had been outlawed in East
Germany in 1969.

On August 23, 1990 the parliament in the palace voted in favour of reunifi-
cation with the Federal Republic. One month later, on September 19, the
same body took the decision to close the palace with immediate effect because
of the asbestos contamination. In 1992 the German Bundestag declared itself
in favour of its demolition. Between 1998 and 2003, specialist companies
cleared the approximately five thousand tonnes of sprayed asbestos from the
building, doing so in a way that would allow the building to be either demolished or renovated afterwards. With the carcinogenic material removed, the
palace was reduced to a shell.

After several architectural competitions to determine the future of the square
which, in 1991, reverted to its original name of "Schlossplatz", the Bundestag
decided in 2003 to have the palace demolished. Between spring 2004 and
the end of 2005 the gutted palace was temporarily re-opened to the public
for cultural events.

In the end, the demolition of the building had to be postponed several times —
in part due to heated protests. Work on dismantling the building finally began
in February 2006. The Swedish steel in the basic structure was melted down;
some was sold to Dubai for use in the construction of the Burj Khalifa, and
some bought by the automotive industry and recycled into engines. Work
on the reconstruction of the historic Berlin City Palace began in March 2013.

She lifted the bundle out of the string bag, unwrapped the cloth
around the asparagus and laid the spears on the kitchen table.
Then she fetched a couple of handfuls of potatoes from the box in
its dark corner next to the refrigerator. Several of them already
had green patches on them, and some had even sprouted short,
knobbly shoots. Evidently the box was not dark enough after all.
The best way, of course, would be to store them in the cellar, but

then they always tasted a bit of coal. She fetched one of the grey tea towels and laid it over the box as if it was a tablecloth.

The hot wash in the washing machine was on its second rinse. With luck it would be dry by the end of the day, as the sun had actually come out at lunchtime. All morning it had been overcast as if it was about to rain any minute.

She peeled the potatoes, slicing off a bit more where the green patches and shoots were, washed and halved them and placed them in a bowl by the cooker. She wanted to have everything prepared in advance as much as possible. At lunchtime she had only made herself some sandwiches, even though it was Sunday. She had never liked cooking just for herself. It simply wasn't worth it.

She had just started rinsing the sand off the asparagus spears when the doorbell rang. She quickly reached for the towel, went out into the hall and opened the door.

"Ah, Marlene, have you got a moment?"

It was Lippe. He lived downstairs across the landing on the first floor.

"Sure. Come in. I just need to finish off in the kitchen quickly."

Lippe had a worn-out look about him. He was a nice, easy-going guy. Sometimes they would all sit together of an evening and have a drink, although not so much lately.

"Holger not back yet?"

He glanced in the living room.

She shook her head. Lippe was studying military medicine, like Holger, but his specialism was stomatology.

He hovered in the doorway.

"Really, Lippe, you could have kept your shoes on, you know."

"Oh well, never mind."

He shrugged his shoulders.

"And the kiddie's having a nap?" He motioned with his head

in the direction of the bedroom. He looked really tired. Perhaps there was something up with Carmen.

"Yes, she's dead to the world. She was knackered. The fresh air. We had quite a long walk."

Straight after lunch she had drawn the curtains and put the child down in her cot. She had babbled for a bit, but soon all was quiet. She had actually been meaning to prepare some lessons, but it had completely slipped her mind in the morning.

"Mmm." He tucked his hands in his trouser pockets. "Jule's asleep too. It's no bad thing, a bit of peace and quiet on a Sunday."

She laid the asparagus spears one after the other on a dry tea towel.

"Queued up for asparagus, too, did you?" He took his hands out of his pockets, folded his arms and grinned broadly.

She couldn't help laughing. She was not the only one pinching asparagus from the field behind the allotments. Green asparagus. She had never once seen it on sale in the shop. Rumour had it that it all went straight to Berlin, to the Palace of the Republic.

"Yes, I hope no-one grasses on us." She dried her hands on the towel and took off her apron.

"Like a drink?"

He was still standing barefoot in the doorway. Lippe was quite a bit shorter than Holger. He had a thick, dark moustache and a receding hairline. His skin was sallow, almost waxy.

"No, no. I won't," he replied. "I'm going to go down to the garden again in a minute."

The Lipperts, like themselves and a few other families from their block, had been allocated a plot in the field behind the new buildings and had cultivated it over the spring months. The soil was very sandy. They had had to cut away the turf with a spade and shake it out before a thin layer of topsoil appeared, and had then planted potatoes to keep the weeds at bay. Lippe had even got hold of some fertiliser from the agricultural cooperative and set up some cold frames, to improve the yield. They had reaped a fairly meagre harvest. But she was glad of whatever she did get. Peppers, radishes, carrots, beans, parsley. They had even managed some strawberries. A small bowlful, but still worth it.

"Come on, let's go in the living room."

He let her past into the hall, she pulled the bedroom door to and went ahead.

The sun now cast a shaft of bright light onto the aquariums, which stood on a homemade shelf unit to the left of the door. They were Holger's fish tanks. Guppies, black mollies, neon tetras and a single catfish that stayed hidden away in its hollow most of the time. To start with they had only had one, but then Holger had kept producing more wooden spindles and sawing more planks, and created space for a second, smaller aquarium above the first, and eventually even a third one, smaller still, right on top. Like a pyramid. The playpen stood in front of the aquariums.

Lippe sat down on the settee. His checked shirt was a bit tight across his stomach. His sleeves were rolled up. His forearms were covered in a dark fur.

"Marlene, we . . ."

He took a deep breath.

Then he sat forward and folded his hands in his lap.

"We deliberated for a long time whether we should tell you."

Strange that he referred to "we", even though he was sitting there on his own in front of her.

He hesitated.

"Well . . . ," he started again, "you know we were in Berlin yesterday. Carmen had a lecture, and I had gone along with Jule. A long old trek, but it was worth it." His right hand was wavering in mid-air.

"Oh yes." She had completely forgotten.

"And afterwards, we thought we'd give ourselves a treat."

He looked over at the window. The cactuses looked really dusty against the light. They could do with watering.

"So we went into the Palace of the Republic, something a bit special, you know."

There was something indecent about his bare feet with their hairy toes on her carpet. She looked at the carved legs of the coffee table. Holger had discovered it a while ago in a derelict house in a neighbouring village. A shabby old thing. You could clearly see the woodworm holes. They would be there for good. The two of them had managed to transport it home by bicycle along the sandy paths through the wood.

"You see, Marlene . . . ," he resumed, straightening his back.

"We saw Holger there. With another woman."

He looked at her now.

"In a compromising situation." He tilted his chin up a fraction, passed his hand over his face and slumped down slightly again.

"We just wanted you to know." It sounded like an apology.

"At first Carmen said it was none of our business." He ran his tongue over his teeth.

"But this morning I said to her: How would you feel if Marlene spotted me somewhere with another woman and didn't say anything?"

A compromising situation? A compromising situation. Poor Lippe. Such a nice guy. Much nicer than Carmen, with her severe plait and her beauty spot, just above her mouth on the left-hand side, which looked as if it had been drawn on.

"I don't know what I'd do either."

His right foot bobbed up and down. "Perhaps you'd like to have a chat with Carmen? You know, woman to woman?"

Carmen was a pharmacist. She had never really felt comfortable in her company.

"I don't think he noticed us," he added.

The table was green. They had painted it themselves. They thought it would be kind of nice.

"Thank you," she said, without knowing why.

Lippe stood up. "I'll get going." He wiped his hands on his trouser legs.

She heard him slip his shoes on in the hall, close the door of the flat and go down the stairs. The dust danced in the light. Actually, the table looked vile.

He twisted round, took his briefcase from the rear seat, laid it on his lap and undid the catch. In amongst his clothes was a water-filled sphere, a present for his daughter. He picked it up.

"Nice," said Achim. "She'll like that."

The greenish water sloshed back and forth. The duck smiled. Holger returned the ball to the briefcase and got out his sandwiches.

"Would you like one?"

He took them out of their greaseproof paper.

Achim turned towards him briefly and shook his head.

"Nah, it's alright." He looked back at the road. There wasn't much traffic.

"I don't want to spoil my appetite."

Holger bit into the sandwich. Spam. The bread tasted old. He had made the sandwiches yesterday morning, while Marlene and the little one were still asleep. To avoid waking them, he had not put his shoes on until he was out in the stairwell, then he had taken the stairs two at a time in his usual way and walked the kilometre to the main road. But an eternity had passed since then. He put the sandwich down and wrapped it up again in the paper.

"Hankering for something proper, are you?"

Achim indicated, stepped on the accelerator and overtook a moped.

Holger wiped his hands on his knees. Only now did he notice how tired he was. His head was hammering. He seldom drank. It just wasn't compatible with the early-morning starts and training. He still had his sports shorts on. Achim had been anxious to get away on time. He probably couldn't wait to see his wife again. After the presentation ceremony he had not even had time to say goodbye to Birgit properly. To be honest, that had suited him.

"Can you just pull over somewhere? I need a piss."

He did not like farewells. He never knew what to say and was glad when it was over.

"Man, you've got the bladder of a girl."

Achim was alright, a bear of a man. Not the fastest, but in long-range hand-grenade throwing he beat the lot of them. From a standing start, and with an action that looked like slow motion. His on-target rate was over 50 per cent.

Achim glanced in the rear-view mirror, let a car overtake, changed down through the gears, indicated and drove a little way along a rough farm track. Then he switched off the engine, took his hands off the steering wheel and turned to face him.

"There you go. All yours!"

Holger got out and went and stood facing the bank. He directed his stream at a patch of stinging nettles. The green hedges were choked with knotweed. Unripe blackberries hung in thorny hedges. Beyond the boundary strip, power lines led directly across the field to a single brick-built farmhouse with a wooden barn and, next to it, a flagpole without a flag. The corn was still green and swayed in the wind. It all looked so peaceful. The combine harvesters would be along at some point though. He felt the sun on the back of his neck.

He found himself thinking about how happy he had been when he had finished school and immediately received permission to embark on a degree. That feeling that now nothing could go wrong. And then his name on the roll of honour. In gothic lettering as on the certificate. His record was still unbroken.

And now? A couple of midges danced around him. He batted them away. If all went to plan, in three years' time he would be a doctor. At least that was something tangible.

"Get a move on, mate."

Of course, Birgit had asked once more when they would see each other again. He hadn't known what to say to that.

He yawned. He pulled up his trousers by the waistband and walked back to the car.

Achim started the engine and set off again. Holger took his tracksuit jacket from the back seat, stuffed it between the seat back and the window frame, and laid his head on it. He looked at Achim. There were little beads of sweat on his forehead. Achim always knew exactly what he wanted. But you didn't have to chat with him the whole time.

Holger turned to the window. Everything looked completely different from the car. He had only ever seen the route from the train.

They drove through a small village with cobbled streets. He looked at the people outdoors. An elderly lady in a house dress standing in her garden, with arms akimbo. A young couple with a pushchair crossing the road. Two boys on bicycles, weaving their way hands-free along the pavement.

Then he closed his eyes. The car vibrated. He tried to relax. He had been in the palace once before, with his parents. Soon after his swearing-in. In a suit even. But he couldn't remember much about it now. Although everyone had talked about it. About the flags, the mirrored glass, the marble, the queues of people.

He didn't know whether it had been his idea or Birgit's. It was just how it worked out. They hadn't had to queue for long either. And then, in the wine bar, they'd even got a table with a view over the Spree. On a Saturday evening too. It had all been so easy. He'd pulled out the chair for her and she'd sat down, as if it were all perfectly normal. Neither of them was appropriately dressed, but they didn't care. Birgit thought they had something to celebrate. Although they hadn't even won. She was the only girl he knew who shaved her armpits.

He opened his eyes and stared at the squashed insects on the windscreen. The assault course was actually the toughest. Once you'd got that over and done with, the worst was out of the way. The water jump and the cross-country run were a walk in the park by comparison.

He straightened up again, wound the window down and leaned his elbow out. The air rushing by felt nice.

Outside, fields and woods went by, telephone masts, a huge tumbledown engine shed, an avenue of lime trees that seemed to go on and on. He was a doctor, though, wasn't he. Or halfway there at least.

He crossed his arms behind his head.

The child stood in the cot with eyes wide open. One hand gripped the bars with fat fingers, the other was reaching over the top rail and flailing in her direction. Her little teeth flashed white in her laughing mouth.

She lifted the little girl up, laid her down on the chest of drawers next to the double bed, peeled off first the babygro, then the plastic pants and lastly the sodden cloth nappy.

The child babbled away, punched the air with choppy movements of her little fists, and kept kicking Marlene's arms and breasts with her bare feet. The padded changing mat was printed all over with yellow teddy bears: one holding a bunch of balloons, one see-sawing in an umbrella, and another riding on a pony. The sequence continually repeating.

She took the toddler, sat her on the potty, went into the kitchen and put the kettle on the stove. Then she opened the wall cupboard, took out the tin of coffee and measured a spoonful of powder into a mug.

When she came back into the bedroom the child was chewing on a corner of the quilt, which had slipped off the double bed. She carefully extracted the saliva-drenched bit of fabric from her mouth, pressed the crocheted toadstool into the child's hand, hoisted the quilt back onto the bed, and smoothed it out with a couple of sweeps of her hand. Then she lifted the little one back onto the mat and wiped her bottom with a damp flannel.

She was just passing the nappy, folded into a triangle, through the child's legs when the kettle started whistling in the kitchen. The toadstool fell to the floor. With a few rapid movements she fastened the nappy and pulled the plastic pants on over it, picked up the little girl in her arms and hurried into the kitchen.

She turned off the gas stove and poured boiling water onto the coffee powder. The child clung to her blouse and pressed her head to her neck. She felt the clenched little hands on her breast. She carried her over to the playpen in the living room and tried to extricate herself from her grasp.

"It's alright," she said. "It's alright," and managed to disentangle herself.

Then she went back into the bedroom, carried the potty to the bathroom, emptied it into the loo, flushed, lowered the lid and sat down.

The window was tilted open. Outside, children were kicking a ball back and forth. Their shouts echoed around the new blocks of flats. She stood up, pushed the curtain aside and looked out. A small boy was dangling upside down from the climbing frame. His hair hung like streaks in the air. A blonde girl wearing glasses, whom she had never seen before, sat alone on the seesaw. She held the handle firmly, stood up, pulled the plank up, let herself fall and crashed down onto a bit of car tyre sticking out of the sand. Then she immediately stood up again, went on tiptoes and let herself drop down again, over and over. Marlene quickly closed the curtain again. The wash ought to be long finished by now.

She opened the drum, hauled the wet things out and stuffed them in the spin dryer over the bath. She used her right hand to hold the lid on firmly, and her left to slide the control knob downwards. The spinner started up. Water sloshed into the bath-tub in several surges, first a big gush, then less each time, a thin, slowly dwindling stream. Once it was producing no more than droplets she let the machine come to a halt.

The rubber ring had slipped out again. She pushed it back, opened the lid and began lifting the laundry out of the spinner one item at a time and hanging it on the clothesline strung across the bathroom. It was mostly cloth nappies, underwear and hand-kerchiefs. There was no way they would be dry by tomorrow. Only last week she had had to strip the sheets in the morning because Holger had wet the bed. Unbelievable.

She closed the lid of the spin-dryer.

She was about to carry the potty back to the bedroom when her gaze alighted on the medals hanging from the oval mirror in the hall. Athletics, decathlon, military multi-sports. Metal dan-gling on colourful ribbons. But she was still so young. She was so young.

She grabbed the medals and yanked them down. They fell to the floor with a clatter. The mirror wobbled but stayed on the wall.

She set the potty down in front of the cot, tilted the window open, went back into the hall and picked up her coffee from the kitchen. Then she carried the mug into the living room, put it down on the green table and flopped down on the settee.

The child was sitting in the playpen with legs wide apart,

crying. Her face was flushed. A string of saliva hung from her mouth. In one of the yellow-lit aquariums, a shoal of iridescent blue neon tetras chased back and forth. Little air bubbles floated up. The guppies had disappeared. The pump hummed steadily. The black-and-white marbled catfish was feeding on the algae on the glass walls with its big suction mouth. Its white-rimmed eyes looked dead. The bedroom door slammed shut.

Her gaze drifted over the rose-patterned wallpaper and the ochre-coloured heater, then along the wall cabinet with the television set and the atlas, the two-volume encyclopaedia and the illustrated books on socialist realism and the Olympic Games, passing over the snake plant and the cactuses on the windowsill and the cushion covers with flower motifs that she had embroidered during her pregnancy. Two small framed prints of sailing boats hung above the sofa. On the table was the fruit bowl Holger had turned on the lathe.

The mug was still full of coffee. She hadn't touched it.

She got up and went to the playpen.

They could see the red light flashing even from afar. It was the crossroads by the Moeckow-Berg radio tower. Then they entered the wood that he knew so well. It immediately turned cool. Holger wound the window up. Achim indicated and pulled over on the right at the bus stop outside the old tollkeeper's house.

"See you tomorrow then."

His fingers skimmed the steering wheel. It had a silvery-shimmering fur cover.

"Thanks, Achim."

Holger reached for his briefcase, opened the door, got out and swung the passenger door shut.

The dark-blue Lada indicated and rejoined the road. Holger watched it go. He tried to remember the numbers and letters of the number plate, but he couldn't. Eventually the car rounded a bend and disappeared into the wood.

He turned around and took the narrow, paved footpath on the left-hand side of the road. A single street lamp stood halfway along the route into the village. It was already lit, even though it was only just beginning to get dark. The old street cobbles shone in its glow.

The row of detached and semi-detached houses began even before the village sign. Roses and delphiniums bloomed in the front gardens. Above the door to a stable-turned-garage, an old horse's harness dangled from a rusty horseshoe. At the filthy bus shelter by the roundabout, a bunch of teenagers were hanging around with their bikes, smoking. Two of them glanced up briefly, gave him an almost imperceptible nod and went back into their huddle. At least they greeted him, even though he lived in one of the army blocks. He crossed the street. He could hear the stream burbling softly behind the hedge. A river helped you get your bearings at least. It was something tangible. Everything was easier when the requirements were clear.

After the bridge his route took him uphill. He turned onto the path behind the church. There was a ladies' black bicycle with a crocheted spoke guard parked in front of the cooperative store. It wasn't even locked. Behind it loomed the outline of the school building. In the left-hand window of the mayor's yellow-painted bungalow, a curtain was pushed slightly to one side. Now you could see the three new blocks of flats too, all staggered. Some of the windows were lit up. This was where the tarmac ended and the sandy footpath began. It had grown cool all of a sudden. He stopped for a moment, took his tracksuit top off his shoulder and put it on.

Lying in between the play apparatus in the playground was a dirty, dented volleyball. The paint had already flaked off the lower bars of the climbing frame, even though it was still quite new, not even two years old. He looked up at the flat. The light was on in the kitchen. The bathroom was dark. What had he expected? He didn't know.

He opened the door and ascended the two flights of stairs, a step at a time. The television was on in Lippe's flat. His footsteps echoed. Outside the Splettstössers' door there was a smell of pea stew.

Her gardening shoes stood next to the doormat. Earth stuck to them, and they were covered with a fine layer of dust. The doormat was askew. He shoved it straight with his feet. The nameplate on the door bore his name, her name, engraved in brass. He was so tired.

He rang the bell, even though he knew his key was in the front pocket of his briefcase. Inside the flat, he heard the sound of the refrigerator door closing. It was an age before the door opened.

She already had her nightie on. She let him hug her, then turned away. He let go of her, put his briefcase down under the coat rack, crouched down and took off his shoes.

"Is the littl'un asleep?"

He looked up at her.

Marlene nodded briefly and disappeared into the kitchen. Everywhere was in darkness. Only the lamp above the kitchen table cast a circle of bright light on the tablecloth.

He slid his feet into his slippers and opened the bedroom door. The child was lying peacefully in her bed, both arms stretched out next to her head. She was breathing in long, regular breaths. He placed his index finger in the little half-open hand. How incredibly contented she looked. Then he pulled the covers up a little, left the room and quietly shut the door. His briefcase was still there at the foot of the coat rack. He picked it up.

When he went to take out the packet containing the sandwiches, he discovered the ball with the duck inside. He took it with him into the kitchen.

Marlene was sitting at the kitchen table with her head tilted back.

"We didn't win, but I've got a present for the littl'un." He placed the ball in front of her on the table. Then he went to the refrigerator, opened the door, looked inside for a moment and closed it again. Next to the sink were some peeled potatoes and green asparagus. He would have liked to make himself a camomile tea, but he didn't dare use the kettle.

He went over to the table, pulled out the chair, sat down, touched her fleetingly on the arm, but then didn't know what to do next and took his hand away again.

Only now did she look at him. He drew his shoulders back and breathed deeply, in and out. Her eyes were almost black.

Lacus Luxuriae
KINAU'S SELENOGRAPHS

* *Gottfried Adolf Kinau, a priest and amateur astronomer from Suhl in Thuringia, dedicated more than thirty years of his life to selenography. His topographical drawings of the moon were much admired by the contemporary lunar research community for their meticulousness.*

† *Only a few of the documents containing Kinau's observations have survived to this day, including his essay* Lunar Rilles *dating from 1848. Of his selenographs, only two had been published in* Sirius, *a journal of popular astronomy, and they are presumed to have been lost to fire, as part of its image collection, during the Second World War.*

In 1932, the International Astronomical Union gave the name "Kinau" to a crater in the southern highlands on the nearside of the moon, as originally proposed by astronomer Edmund Neison in 1876. Who's Who in the Moon, *a handbook of lunar nomenclature published in 1938 by the British Astronomical Association, contains the following entry:* C. A. Kinau (?–1850). Botanist and selenographer. He had an official post on the estate of the Prince of Schwarzenberg in southern Bohemia, and published in 1842 two works on Poisonous Plants and Fungi. *Despite a worldwide search, no botanist by the name of Kinau could be found. In 2007, he was replaced in the U.S. survey authority's records by the priest Gottfried Adolf Kinau as the man who gave his name to the crater. To this day, no trace has ever been found of C. A. Kinau.*

Knowing when and under which constellations I was born does little to illuminate the subject of our investigation. Suffice it to mention that my entry into the earthly world fell on one of those annually recurring nights in which the Leonids reveal themselves, in one of the most impressive celestial light spectacles visible to the naked eye, at least back in the days when the blackness of the night had not yet been diluted to a perpetual twilight by the glare of gas lamps and their inglorious successors. One year, as a young student, I was treated to a blazing shower of shooting stars around the time of my birthday, a festive rain of fire which soon filled the entire firmament with innumerable flaring meteors and planted in me that invisible seed which would eventually germinate some decades hence and bring forth the most passionate blossom: my love of the starlit night, of the planets and their satellites, which is what ultimately led me to that certainly higher, yet also undeniably remote sphere which I am now obliged to call my home.

At first, though, I was seized – a natural consequence of my rural upbringing – by a penchant for botany, and there awakened in me a fervent desire, on completion of my studies in Advanced Forestry, to acquire a permanent paid position with a broad scope that would enable me to advance my research.

I found it in my local vicinity as an administrator for the southern estates of His Highness Prince Johann Adolf zu Schwarzenberg, the second to bear this name, and as such my role was initially to oversee the leasehold farm of Bzy, then the Forbes estate, two tracts of land particularly exposed to the adverse effects of their unprotected location on the right bank of the Moldau, until the reform instituted by the supreme authorities dispatched me to the central seat of princely power, namely the large castle perched on a steep rock above the Moldau in the town of Krumau. I grew fond of this region, despite its harsh, damp climate with its early and late frosts, for which the fertile but weather-beaten soil barely compensated, especially since agricultural conditions became increasingly testing, the closer the lands of this sprawling territory were to the Bohemian Wood – a vast forest whose quasi-primeval interior was inhabited by wild bears.

In addition to that activity, which I performed with the single-minded zeal characteristic of young provincial officials of the pre-1848 period, I dedicated my few free hours deliberately not to the fodder plants and crops that dominated the agricultural cycle, but to the wayward phenomena of toxic flora, having since my young days felt a particular attraction to those plants which bring no benefit to mankind, but rather tend to cause harm to people and their livestock. What captivated me most of all about them was the mysterious way in which they worked, seemingly according to a wholly obscure system that manifested no firm features whatsoever by which one might have distinguished these often life-threatening plants from benign ones, for one and the same family frequently included both non-toxic species – even edible vegetables – and ones that induced breathing difficulties and vomiting. In those days, fungi formed an important part of the diet of the rural Bohemian community; mothers used to place bunches of *Solanum nigrum* in their babies' cradles to help them sleep or, rather, forcibly send them off to sleep; herbalists every-where carried on their deadly trade in sacred *Anemone pulsatilla*; and every now and again some simpleton lured by their beauty into partaking of the glossy black fruits of the *Atropa belladonna* would find himself struck down by raving madness.

So I collected and examined the plants which grew in abun-dance along footpaths and streams, on heaths and in meadows, studied the burned entrails of livestock that had come to grief following a fateful indulgence, and filled my observation journals, all with the worthy aim of publishing a compendium of the poi-sonous plants of Bohemia and a paper on the fungi found in this part of the country – some of them eminently edible, but many more of them toxic. The study of cryptogamia, long-neglected at the time and admirably revived by Krombholz only a short time previously, was an activity that would prepare me like no other for my subsequent field of endeavour: the unseen work of legacy preservation.

The results of my research were favourably received, notwithstanding the fact that no general underlying principles could be deduced from my observations. An amiable scientific dialogue ensued, and as a newly elected member of several learned societies I soon came to regard myself as one of the select circle of those who have added to our knowledge of the world, even in a discipline as lowly as botanical classification. They were good times. I botanised, oversaw the accounts of the princely estate, excelled both as a strict supervisor and an eager subject, and took a fancy to a woman who reciprocated my affection to a sufficient degree that I was not deterred from making my proposal. The years went by; grain harvest was followed by corn threshing, hop picking by fruit harvest, green fodder distribution by beet sowing, and meanwhile the numerous measures I had taken to maximise the amount of arable land available proved as effective as intended: woods were cleared, heathland cultivated, moors drained and ponds emptied down to their peaty bottom. With my attention so focused on the future and on practical considerations, my research gradually ground to a halt during this time, and the more closely I scrutinised the natural world through my magnifying glass, the more it seemed to me in every one of its countless metamorphoses to embody unbridled chaos untameable by any governing hand – a phenomenon familiar to anyone seeking to unite theory and practice. One goes to great lengths to organise and configure this chaos in one's mind, only to confuse the scientific picture just when one believes oneself to be enriching it.

And so the glorious vision of an all-encompassing system became bound up in my heart with an unspeakable feeling of worthlessness, bitterly fuelled by a series of flagrant offences against forest laws. Every mangled trunk was a thorn in my side, the flesh around it festering with a sense of injured pride – the poison of weakness, which I endeavoured to dispel on lengthy forays into the forest, which gradually became my habit in place of attending church. Indeed it was on a Sunday, as I roamed the impenetrable undergrowth of the Bohemian Wood as was my wont, making my way into its dark heart of nothing but spruces, where all the tree debris blown down by the wind had caused bare patches littered with dead trunks which lent the wood an almost wounded appearance, that, visited by a peculiar fear that I am inclined in hindsight to call prophetic, I pulled from the ground the frond of an especially magnificent fern, and on closer exam- ination it became apparent that the roots of the regal plant pre- sented the shape of a waning crescent moon, no less. This moment, which has since haunted me like a vision, was embedded in a solemn silence uninterrupted by any song, call or indeed the slightest sound from any bird. And as if this unmistakable sign, which I was immediately willing to acknowledge as the mark of a higher power, did not already weigh heavily enough on my soul, only a few days later – in the early hours of July 8, 1842 – the big circle of the moon cast its grey-blue shadow over me, although my place of abode at the time was not granted the pleasure of a total eclipse of the sun, something that one would have been able to witness a mere hundred miles further south. When, on that day, the fireball narrowed to a thin sliver and its now deathly pale light transfigured the courtyard, the poultry fell silent again and fled to their coop, while all my blood rushed vertiginously to my heart, and all at once it struck me with glittering clarity that anyone wishing to scale the sturdy botanical branch of the tree of science all the way to its outermost fork must reach up towards the mighty phenomena of the all-overarching sky. No sooner had

I embarked on my new studies than the logicality of turning from plants sprouting in obscurity to the secret order of the stars became for me a fortifying certainty. After all, throughout the ages, the vast majority of alchemists had been botanists first and foremost, and the most prominent alchemists had simultaneously been astrologers and astronomers, like the architect of that compelling theory which posits that every plant has its own heavenly twin in the form of a star. The degree to which the study of poisons and the study of the heavens are intertwined is manifest not least in that verse from the Book of Revelation, unfathomable at that time, which had predicted the fatal impact of the comet Wormwood, known to have wiped out a third of the Earth's population as well as the D.N.A. quartz glass archives designed to last for ever, consequently rendering our work here all the more urgent, although our activities have very wisely always been confined to those goods generally classified as analogue, and not those belonging to that ephemeral, electrical device-dependent state between zero and one. In those days the human race, fooled by its confidence in the infallibility of its supreme ingenuity, experienced once again the most appalling consequences of its lack of knowledge. The Earth was not a safe place and never would be.

Within the space of a year not only was I wholly familiar with celestial phenomena, I had also discovered my special liking for the closest of all the heavenly bodies, deriving unprecedented pleasure from studying its scarred form in detail and devoting myself nightly to the gradual discovery and detailed drawing of its peculiarly damaged yet chastely shimmering surface, which I learned to examine through a five-inch refractor with a focal length of three feet that I had purchased in Budweis, in the same way as I had once examined spores concealed in tender membranes. For that which is near is far off – and the higher truth is revealed in the most inconspicuous of creatures and the most remote – both under the microscope and through the telescope. Given that my previous labour of love had been concerned with outlying phenomena, it is not surprising that, with my new subject too, it was primarily its outermost edges that fascinated me, in other words those regions which, due to the slightly swaying proper motion of the moon in accordance with some complex law, may be glimpsed only in certain phases. The cratered landscape of Tycho with the incomparable shadows it casts at sunset, Plato, the circular mountain range, in the early dawn hours, Gassendi, the banked plateau close to the light limit, and the evenly shaped bowl of Linné were to me what Cicero, Seneca and Virgil were to Petrarch: faithful friends and mute recipients of my nightly monologues. Not that they ever answered me. The moon is notoriously silent by nature. Yet it was a gracious silence, which, unlike that of the prince's smug attendants, did not punish me with con-tempt, but seemed to reward each one of my rapt looks with benevolence and kindness.

Henceforward I lived each day only for the night, longed for its blackness which obliterated the earthly realm and caressed the starlight, and for the dark time of year, when the early sunset would allow me to neglect my worldly duties and silently devote that time to my new master.

Very few are prepared to go as far as I went, for it takes not audacity but humility to exchange people's memory of you and the secure career of a civil servant for the vague prospect of attaining some higher truth or greater glory. To disappear, as long as one person remembers you, demands considerable skill, all the more so if you hold a highly responsible position on an estate like Krumau which, even after the fateful year when the authorities had to suffer the loss not only of serf labour but also of some of their best goods, still ranked as one of the most pre-eminent in the realm. The prince was known for visiting his estates year in, year out, watching them thrive like a father watching over his children, hence he followed my activities, too, with fond suspicion, since I was fatherless and only a few years younger and could have been his brother, or perhaps actually was, as my mother hinted to me on her death bed. Her funeral would be followed by other, more painful ones, until I elected never again to have to embark on this most harrowing of all processions, and, of my own accord, chose the fate that overtakes us all one day, since it was now of no consequence whether my name were to fade to illegibility forthwith or only in four or forty-four generations' time. Circumstances favoured my undertaking more than they hindered it: the lands under my administration were now considerably smaller in area, and the two children who would have been able to carry tidings of me to future generations lay in the graveyard, borne off by plagues which my wife, labouring under an ineradicable misconception, ascribed, along with the catastrophic failed harvests of those years, to the sinister influence of the moon, and I was unable either to disabuse her or to ease her pain, which bore a silent reproach. She in turn could not abide my moon addiction – and possessed neither parents nor siblings who could have mourned or been suspicious of her abrupt passing. In any case, it was not possible, under the prevailing laws of nature, for me to take her with me; each one of us must leave everything behind, as if he were crossing the final threshold.

I landed, like all those before and after me, in the Mare Imbrium, the sunless lake, naked and freezing, fighting for breath, as befits a birth. As soon as the decreed quarantine period had elapsed, I was appointed as an assistant, and hence the lowest member of what seemed to me to be a completely and utterly perfect institution. Inspired by the irresistible regularity of its routines, I took care faithfully to perform all tasks entrusted to me, the most lofty of these duties consisting in the preliminary sorting of all incoming goods.

As everyone knows, Ariosto, in his *Orlando Furioso*, once set abroad a rumour that everything that is lost on Earth ends up here with us on the moon, an idea he had copied almost word for word from Alberti, who had previously overheard it from a muddleheaded washerwoman in Padua. Truly all three were over-indulging their imagination if they thought to find in this fabled place everything they themselves secretly missed: bygone days and fallen empires, long-lost loves and unanswered prayers.

The truth is that the centrifugal forces act in the opposite direction, just as it is not the Earth that keeps the moon in its orbit, but the moon that keeps the terrestrial body in *its*, which is why the moon essentially merits the title of mother planet, or at the very least that of the Archimedean point from which the world may be lifted off its axis. For the Earth is nothing, and the moon in its appalling feigned dependence, that mute, calcified mirror, is everything, especially since it is in any case only a matter of time before the cosmic page turns and Earth's satellite finally assumes the dominant role in this fragile configuration, a role it has covertly played since its very origin. For it is invariably the servant who places an obligation on the master – and not the reverse, as my experience as a mediator between the domestic staff and the prince taught me on multiple occasions.

My relocation happened to coincide with the first crude experiments by the physiologist Mayer, which suggested that movement and warmth are merely different manifestations of one and the same force, and that consequently any loss of energy is a near-impossibility. This basic principle of energy conserva-tion – which here on the moon had been known since time immemorial as the law of loss avoidance – governs the extensive interactions between the two stars and implies that anything that

arrives here on the moon disappears on Earth, having been
selected by an independent Moon/Earth Council on the basis
of a fair yet ultimately impenetrable principle, before finding its
way into this world and hence crossing into that weightless
intermediate realm of the archive, which eludes the traditional
assignment to either the living or the dead.

Only for a brief, yet glorious period now in the distant past
were all incoming items kept without exception. If one believes
the myriad stories passed down by word of mouth despite the
prohibitions, these included the stones of the Olmecs; a clay
model of the Cretan labyrinth from the workshop of the historical figure Daedalus; a vase depicting the feast of Hybristica
held in Argos in honour of the Muses' servant Telesilla, at which
the women would wear men's clothes and the men women's
clothes; the magnificent nose of the Sphinx of Giza; the second
Arabic translation of the *Almagest*, inscribed in gold lettering on
a 220-foot-long dragon gut, as well as Euripides' play *Polyidus*
with its line that shines out across the darkness of oblivion:
"Who knows whether life is death and death is life?" – a line that
seems to me to express most admirably that to which we are
elected or condemned here; also half a dozen atomic bombs preserved in Greenland's ice; a neat crucifix made out of the cross-
bone of a frog's head; several complete, but entirely different
sounding transcripts of the *Secretum Secretorum*; Simone Martini's
elaborate portrait of Petrarch's beloved Laura de Noves, which
apparently served only to prove how conceited the much vaunted
beauty was in reality; the grotesque codices of the Maya, which
could be read only by their priests and by no-one else, along
with a remarkable number of works by women, whose titles alas
I can no longer recall.

That era was followed by a time of transition in which the task
of selection and safekeeping was entrusted to an army of chosen

ones, which included some of the greatest experts in the art of memory, who had been unable to escape the call to our sphere, until they were replaced by some equally great experts in the art of forgetting, since it had gradually dawned on those in charge that the latter were more adept at managing the flow of incoming goods.

It was much like on Earth: each generation reorganised the goods, every new regime, for its own edification, invented a whole new approach, and if practical activity declined under one ruler, theory, by contrast, blazed all the more brightly. Periods of deliberate neglect were followed by spells of excessive concern, and the oft-raised objection that, while much was achieved in both, even more was omitted, fails to take into account the immense challenge posed by the general space problem which hangs over every archive from the hour of its birth, which no system yet invented is able to solve, particularly considering that space here is limited to an area not much larger than the Russian Empire when it was at its most extensive.

On one occasion the order was issued to adopt the model of a permanent but limited library as the basis for goods storage, while another time the originals were replaced with improved, scaled-down copies, until it emerged that the material selected did not possess all the specific qualities advisable for an undertaking of this magnitude, and soon some of the most wonderful photocopies became unusable and were disposed of as expertly as their fragile originals before them.

The council's directives frequently met with astonishment on the part of the lunar population, which was not, in fact, composed of the most worthy representatives of the human race, but rather resembled an arbitrarily thrown-together community of disparate people with nothing in common save for the tender bonds they had once forged with Earth's satellite, which from a distance presented itself in an entirely different light in each of their respective cultures. Indeed the moon, which, in accordance with both my native languages, I have only ever been able to conceive of as masculine, had charmed more than a few of the administrators here as the seductive Madame Luna; it even appeared to the Manchu as a divine rabbit holding a mortar, and alas occasionally it also – in keeping with the English expression – tempted lunatics and somnambulists into staying here. The madmen showed themselves to have a particular fondness for the wanton custom of reciting in seemingly never-ending songs the names of those monuments that had already fallen victim to the malignant action of the solar wind, an incantatory practice that continued through the long lunar nights, something that some, and not solely the most depraved of our colleagues, would pay for with the abrupt end of their eternal life, if one is disposed to refer to what we have here in those terms. A complete absence of history is the highest virtue in this life; not the feeblest remnant of earthly melancholy is tolerated here on high, and anyone who nonetheless falls prey to it forfeits his existence here, since the lunar archivist, more even than any terrestrial curator, is required to treat each object equally and, in the interests of all, must not become emotionally attached to any of the goods, particularly as the greedy ravages of time in any case allow only a fraction of the material to maintain its original form for a certain period.

Needless to say, the allocations from the council were never-ending, and soon forever relegated any efforts to preserve all goods – including the creation of an indelible memory containing everything that ever has been and will be – to the realm of impossibility, along with any prospect of a return to Earth, which turned serenely like a white-clouded marble before our eyes, having not the slightest inkling of our labours. I was not alone in finding this sight increasingly hard to bear. And so, when my long-awaited promotion finally came to pass, I was able, without encountering any appreciable resistance, to implement my plan to relocate the archive initially to the side facing away from the planet, and eventually to move it entirely underground. Demoralised and spurred on in equal measure by the failure of my predecessors, I created there, in the lightless depths of the Lacus Luxuriae, a system whose supposedly illustrious centrepiece consisted in the directive henceforward only to retain goods that made reference to the moon, this seeming to me the most worthy approach, if only for the reason that in the works destined for Earth's satellite, the story of the self-absorbed planet forever turning on its own axis is replicated like the product of a dream. For, as Aristotle once suggested, the dream and the cesspit are inseparably bound to one another, and the moon, like the bowel from which dreams emerge, is the true seat of the soul, nurtured by the longings of our lunar confraternity, like a cheerful, diverse population of simple-minded, insatiable bacteria.

It was an indescribable blessing to be rid of all those goods we had been keeping which had committed the unforgivable error of not mentioning our homeland, the moon, at least once – if only in the improper, metaphorical sense of the Romantics or their numerous successor movements. Those items that had measured up to my strict selection criteria and survived the tumult of long-established regulations were admitted to the Lunarium. The centrepieces of the innermost department were a Babylonian canon of eclipses, an album of Japanese ink drawings of pink protuberances, a strange silent film called *The First Men in the Moon*, a mechanical musical box containing a Selene riding on a gilded centaur, the print template of Galileo's *The Starry Messenger*, in which he likens the shape of a moon crater to that of my homeland Bohemia, along with vast quantities of lunar rock recovered in response to repatriation requests, to which some notable improvements were made in the course of my negotiations. In short, this seemed like a splendid arrangement, until the time came when I ruled, in my professed wisdom, that it was no longer sufficient just to mention the moon; rather it was necessary for it to be referred to in its true sense, since, after all, even the most brilliant lunar theories had always suffered from the flaw that, in the moon, they were only really looking for the Earth, only wanted to see in it their own inadequate self, a small, stunted twin, the remnant of that prehistoric cataclysm when the fledgling Earth collided with a nameless planet – the event that sparked life itself – and a piece was violently ripped from it which, as a satellite, settled into its own orbit, a late-born, wayward copy, a blind mirror, a star gone cold.

Oh, if only I had moderated my mania! For when I examined the stores of items again, between the Nebra sky disc and an early wax relief of the lunar mountains crafted by Wilhelmine Witte, wife of Court Councillor Witte, I happened upon a bundle of selenographs which, to my silent horror, were signed with my own name in an unknown hand. Kepler must have felt similar emotions when he came face to face with his demon in a dream. In me, likewise, all manner of sensations were awakened which I thought I had left behind on Earth, since in those drawings, which betokened more diligence than talent, I encountered again the mountain formations I had long idolised, the sight of which had shaken me less when in their immediate vicinity than when I used to observe them from afar, an activity to which I had devoted the best of my years on Earth. And so, from behind the veil of oblivion, a memory re-emerged of that blessed afternoon on which an unusually favourable opportunity had arisen, on account of the secondary earthshine, to observe the night side of my present place of work and to record it in drawings: Aristarchus shone brightly, the Mare Humorum stood out with dark clarity,

Grimaldi appeared greyish black, and, as I savoured the aftertaste of the memory jogged from its slumber, I was again overcome by that long-dormant urge that had once brought me to this remote place, to this labyrinth of lightless caverns with its interlocking villous aisles, a place where – it now irrefutably dawned on me – the object of my highest admiration had become for me one of daily chores, and the radiant future had faded away into an inaccessible past. Only the present, the tender blossom of the moment, had always contrived to hide itself from me.

There I was, at the pinnacle of my life's work, in the supposedly legitimate possession of supremely precious goods, from which the ghosts of my past joys and most recent sufferings drifted up to me, sensitive as an exposed nerve. The body in which I had, not long ago, considered myself as safe as in my mother's womb, had suddenly turned cold, my high-mindedness had vanished and I felt a strong antipathy towards the prospect of uselessly repeating over and over like Sisyphus the task already performed countless times, since none of the future methods would be able to banish the thought that only now was ripening in me to a sad certainty: that the moon, like every archive, was not a place of safekeeping, but one of total destruction, Earth's own knacker's yard, and the only practicable way of saving my foolish work, the Lunarium, from the inevitable – its certain replacement by infinitely stricter and better conceived systems – was for me to pre-empt the downfall that awaited it myself.

To understand the moon means to understand oneself, and today, at the very limit of my wretched existence, I can make so bold as to say that I have succeeded in this to some small degree, though that realisation did not, like the vast majority of truths, also serve to alleviate the pain it engendered but, on the contrary, the sheer size of the dose turned the medicine to poison. This insight gained too late tastes as bitter as the semi-ripe fruits of the nightshade. The moon has stayed the same, and the universe with its constantly twinkling lights of long-extinguished stars is the eternally old, historic place. I was a person like any other for whom the moon, like an ever-painful phantom limb, was merely a reminder of a now-lost state of perfection, of the immeasurable trauma of birth, whose raw violence inherently presents more of a riddle than ineluctable death itself. But because remembering can be learned, whereas forgetting cannot, I am denied the possibility of returning home, or of finding sanctuary in a belief in Linné's classification or in Jesus on the cross, which is what saved my doppelgänger from my fate. So I am departing a life that is no longer deserving of its name, and perhaps never was, and an occupation which, strictly speaking, was no more point-less than any other. The terrible thing, I now know, has already happened and any terror to come is only the inevitable conse-quence of the beginning of all time, including the hour, so near and yet so far, when the central luminary – the sun – will burn up and all the celestial bodies associated with it will be vaporised. How I wish the remains of my mortal shell would go the same way as that tall spruce in Tusset wood, which was felled by lumberjacks while still healthy and in its 125th year, but whose trunk they were unable either to cut up or to process as no saw could be found that was large enough to span the width of the shaft, so that they were left with no choice but to leave the col-ossal trunk to rot where it lay. For whereas on Earth the rotten body of every toppled trunk is soon colonised by the richest flora of mosses and fungi, and decay fuels the cycle of life with a constant ardour, in the lunar disposal craters no rebirth awaits, but merely a disintegration into fine grey electrically charged dust – an irreversible process uniquely aided by the extremely thin, vacuum-like atmosphere of this place.